Nurse, the Bedpans are out of Alignment

Nurse, the Bedpans are out of Alignment

Memories of Bart's
Student Nurses –
February 1965 Set

Compiled by
Elaine Steane MBE

ISBN: 978-1-913663-00-1

Book design by Marion Stockton

Produced in the UK by Biddles Books Ltd.

Please direct all enquiries to Elaine Steane: e.fullardsteane@gmail.com

---

Night Duty, wood engraving (opposite) by Simon Brett

Simon lived at Bart's from the time he was five years old. He is the son of Antony Brett, the Steward of the Hospital. The Steward's Office was under the arch at the entrance into the hospital square. It was a live-in job. The family had flat above the Hogarth staircase, the traditional Steward's house having been destroyed in the Blitz. After Mr Brett's retirement the ancient office of Steward was suspended and its duties shared out among various NHS managers.

This book is dedicated to
Jean Gaunt, Gill Hayward
and Katie Lees.

Night Duty

Contents

Foreword

In 1965 a group of eager young women met for the first time at Preliminary Training School (PTS) at Radlett in Hertfordshire. A bond was struck there. We all started together and faced the anxiety and the excitement of going up to Bart's and learning to be nurses. Throughout the first three years of our training we again grouped together during the month-long academic sections of each year. These were formative years and the bond has remained.

We have had several regular reunions and most of the 'February 1965 Set' has turned up to each. For a short time, when we are together, we are those young women again.

Special thanks to Elaine Steane, née Fullard, for the idea, the initiation, impetus and organisation of this book. In January 2010, just a week before our 45 year reunion, Elaine wrote around to the members of our Set to ask for 'the best, the worst and funniest moments' of our time at Bart's including our entrance interviews. This was triggered after Anne Runciman and Elaine compared being asked about whether we had helped our mothers with housework by Matron who interviewed us, then being asked to strip naked for a medical examination! Anne's comment was that at that point she wished she'd opted to go to St Thomas' where all you had to do was to write an essay on 'Why I chose Nursing'. A mystery that we nearly solved but failed in the end, was why candidates had to climb up on a chair and either open or shut a skylight window alternately? Jackie McDevitt, in her memories, gets the closest to explaining this.

We gathered these photocopied documents and now, 10 years later, we have got them between covers as a record for our families, friends and the wider world to learn a snapshot of what it was like to train at such a famous hospital in the 1960s, but also the tremendous gain of life-long friendship between us.

Stephanie Ryland, née Norbury

Acknowledgements

It is a proof of the friendship, the camaraderie, and the fun that we as the 'February 1965 Set' have that so many of the us were willing to put pen to paper at short notice, then later on to supply photographs that has created this very special collection. They not only record our anxious beginnings and progress through training, but also how all encompassing it was both physically and mentally. Sincere thanks to all who contributed and those who have verbally added the highs and the lows of our four years together, as well as those who helped answer my many queries.

Thank you to Marion Stockton for her publishing services of copy editing, proofreading, design and make-up, plus additional research which has pulled these memoirs together so professionally.

Back at home, my trusty colleague Katie Burt has meticulously proof-read and enjoyed the entries as they arrived from parts of the UK and beyond. I so appreciate her patience and tenacity in the final editing.

As ever, thank you to John, my archaeologist husband, who, despite not having a medical brief, spotted anomalies!

Elaine Steane, née Fullard

St. Bartholomew's Hospital

REGULATIONS FOR STUDENT NURSES

Training begins at the Preliminary Training School. Candidates on entry should be at least 18½, and not more than 30 years of age.

They must produce evidence of good moral character, good health, unimpaired faculties, and general fitness of disposition and temperament for the duties of a Sick Nurse, and they should be of at least 5 ft. 2 ins. in height and of good physique.

After passing the examination at the end of the Preliminary Training School Course, there is a trial period of two to three months in the Wards of the Hospital. On completion of this trial period, if elected, they engage to remain in training at the Hospital for a period of four years from date of entry to Preliminary Training School, training to include one year after passing the Final Hospital Examinations. They will not be allowed to withdraw before the expiration of that term, except on special grounds approved by the Board of Governors.

Uniform is provided by the Hospital, with the exception of shoes and stockings.

It is not considered suitable for ornamental spectacles to be worn with uniform.

Laundry is done free of expense.

The following training allowances will be made subject to deductions for Health and National Insurance, and superannuation contributions. £~~128~~ 135 per annum is deducted for board and lodging during residence.

1st year	£~~299~~ 325
2nd year	£~~345~~ + £5 after passing Preliminary State Examination.
3rd year	£~~336~~ 365
4th year £365	£~~396~~ until State Registration.
Then	£~~525~~ 600 Staff Nurses' salary. (Board lodging deduction £~~100~~ 200).

or any increase recommended by the Whitley Council.

Student Nurses are resident in the Nurses' Homes.

Student Nurses registered on any supplementary part of the State Register will receive such additional training allowances as are recommended by the Whitley Council.

Student Nurses will be required to attend lectures, classes, demonstrations and, if thought advisable, coaching classes.

At the end of the fourth year a Certificate of competency as Nurses will be awarded to those Student Nurses who besides having discharged their Ward duties efficiently have passed the Final Hospital Examination and the Final State Examination. Such Certificate may be a First Class Honours Certificate, a Second Class Honours Certificate or a Pass Certificate.

They will be required to conform to the general rules of the Hospital, as well as such regulations specially affecting the Student Nurses as may be made from time to time, and they will be required to take duty in any department of the Hospital at the discretion of the Matron.

They will be subject to termination of training at any time for misconduct, inefficiency or repeated neglect of duty.

The health of the Nursing Staff is under the care of a Physician specially appointed for the purpose, and such specialists as may be consulted.

Before acceptance applicants will be required to undergo a medical examination. A certificate of vaccination within 6 months of entry and a dental certificate within 1 month of entry, will be asked for after acceptance.

Piggott's Manor Piggott's Manor at Letchmore Heath, Hertfordshire was the Preliminary Training School for St Bartholomew's Hospital from 1948 to 1971. It was then purchased by Beatle, George Harrison, in 1973 who donated it to the International Society for Krishna Consciouness.

Aldenham Cottage Aldenham Cottage, Letchmore Heath was home for the student nurses at PTS.

Beth Allen

Who can forget Nancy Sinatra singing *These Boots are Made for Walking*, and the Righteous Brothers being played very loudly at PTS?

And why did we have to learn to lay a tray properly as though we were Lyons Coffee House bunnies?

I remember having to bend over when we were being measured for our uniforms. Heaven forbid we should show the back of our knees!

I seem to recall a lot of night duty, especially wall washing in theatres. In fact I really disliked theatres having dropped a whole tray of CSSD (Central Sterile Services Department) instruments on the floor during an operation. The surgeon was not impressed.

In the grounds of PTS L–R: Ruth Shrubbs, Beth Allen and Sylvia Bennett.

One amusing memory I have is that following a stint of night duty, Maggie, Mary and I went by train to Yugoslavia and were in stitches talking about night sisters. We were sharing a carriage with three women who turned out to be night sisters at St Thomas', so they heard every word!

Who else remembers interminable hours in the milk kitchen on nights, making up the formula for the babies?

Late passes were a bugbear. It was easier not to get one, stay out all night and whip past the gate porter in the early morning. Genius!

Weight loss was important, and the really cool girls could get aprons that overlapped at the back! And the smaller you could make your hat the better it was.

Does anyone else remember the first time you were called Staff Nurse? How wonderful. And wearing a blue belt with a buckle. I've still got mine but it doesn't meet!

Jean Gaunt's room was a meeting place after nights. Coffee and cigarettes. Her room must have been a health hazard!

Wonderful times, we were so lucky.

Chris Bailey

I had always wanted to be a nurse. As a small child my favourite game was playing at doctors and nurses! My mother always encouraged us children to aim high – be the best. So I was thrilled to get an interview at Bart's and even more delighted to be accepted. I lived at Aldenham Cottage and shared a room with Dorf and Pat. I remember being 'weighed in' on our first day and after three months of home cooking and delicious desserts I was astounded at the amount of weight I'd gained! Hardly surprising of course! I remember PTS as being a time of total harmony. We laughed, we bonded and we got to know each other pretty well.

Things were to change. My first ward was Smithfield, men's medical. I found Sister Smithfield a bit of a cold fish and frightfully proper. I was a bit frightened of her. One of my tasks was to check the spittoons – a sickening job. I have a very vivid memory of one patient taking great pride in showing me what he had produced from his nose one afternoon when I returned from a split duty! I still retch at the thought of it!

I took over from Anne Runciman as the junior on Fleet Street Ward. She had nursed a man after a shunt and he was soon to be discharged to convalescence in Hastings. I promised to look after him as she had done and once he'd left the

Room mates L–R: Pat Churchman, Dorf Clarkson and Chris Bailey.

ward Elaine and I hitched down to Hastings to visit him on our day off! He was very touched. Speaking of Elaine – on another occasion I had gone with Elaine to her home. It must have been summer because it was warm and sunny. We played tennis. During the course of the game I fell and hurt my arm. Her Mum lent me a beautiful scarf to use as a sling and we returned to Bart's, me in excruciating pain. I went to Casualty. I had broken my arm. I was attended by the most gorgeous Senior Reg! After plastering my arm I was settled in sick rooms and felt very unhappy. I must have been sent home to recuperate.

I really blotted my copybook as a staff nurse! The circumstances are vague now but on a rather quiet night I decided to give the nurse in charge on Casualty Ward something to do. I organised for myself to be wheeled across the square on a trolley and pretend to be a patient! As luck would have it Night Sister was visiting at that moment. I was hauled up in front of Miss Harper, the Deputy Matron. She had always been very sympathetic towards me. She let me off with a caution and asked if I'd given any thought as to how my poor widowed mother would feel if I'd been asked to leave Bart's because of a silly prank!

I suppose everyone remembers my affair with Fernando! I was so madly in love! I remember I cried all night the day he left and went back to Majorca. I did hear from him again; he wished me well and supposed I was married by now. I didn't reply as I was married then.

Sylvia Bennett

My memory of Bart's comes back in a series of flashbacks or snapshots. The mention of the interview immediately took me back to the trepidation I felt going to Matron's office. Bart's was the pinnacle and where I wanted to go. This was my first interview and the details escape me but I do remember being asked to shut the window and my bewilderment when I found out that all the other candidates had been asked to do the same; the relevance still totally escapes me.

My next memory is of going to PTS. The train journey from Baker Street, looking at all the other young women and wondering if they were going too, and trying to see if they were clutching an umbrella and looking nervous.

Collecting our uniform was a revelation. I will never forget Mary Tuckwell standing in front of me while her hat was made, that large starched square folded and pleated; it came just above her eyebrows and her dress just above her ankles! Amazing how much smaller they became as time went by.

I remember lots of fun and laughter as well as work; dressing up the skeleton; saying good morning to Miss Piggott, one of the training dummies, before any procedure on her, was hard to do with a straight face. Allen and Bennett made a good team!

Sylvia Bennett.

Going on the wards came so quickly, Rees-Mogg men's surgical was my first experience, I was terrified of Sister. I could never get the lovely men to drink enough water so they called me 'Water Lily'. Luckily the real 'power' in the ward took pity on me and would remind me of the things I had forgotten. This was, of course, Lil the ward cleaner who kept the ward spotless – Sister deferred to her. I also had Irene to keep me on the straight and narrow and this was the start of a friendship that is as strong today as then.

The next few years passed so quickly.

Highs and lows – hard work to high standards, respect, the overwhelming tiredness of night duty, and grief when a dear patient you had nursed died. Lots of good friends, laughter, exploring the Swinging Sixties and fashions, and companionship with always one of the Set to talk to when the problems and pressures got too much.

There were some wonderful social occasions – what excitement and planning outfits for Matron's Ball, later the Galleon Club, introducing boyfriends, parties, 21st birthdays, and then weddings.

I think we were very lucky to have found such a wonderful Set of girls to train with and, remarkably, after fifty-five years we are all drawn back to celebrate the February 1965 Set.

I have always been proud to have been trained to the standards of excellence demanded by Bart's and overjoyed when John and I delivered our eldest daughter Katherine to the Bart's Medical school at the start of her road to becoming a Consultant. She too has a 'Bart's Set'!

Anne Berry

I remember good friends, fun and a lot of laughter, but there was a serious side. We all saw some pretty hairy stuff by today's standards, but thinking back, we took it for granted.

Memories of my interview

I remember an awe-inspiring person in a white frilly hat, not Miss Loveridge. Luckily the telephone rang at a crucial point, she forgot the question, and I was accepted.

Memories of training

Good friends, lots of laughter, sometimes hysterical. Hero worship of a kind staff nurse. Inspiration to be a Pink (5th year) finally achieved in my beloved theatres, a dream come true!

Despair, night duty! Eight nights on, such a long stretch!

The work of Mr Ellison-Nash with spina bifida babies; closing the spinal defect, inserting shunts for hydrocephalus.

Children with retinoblastoma – sometimes several children in a family – before the days of genetics. How kind Sister Radcliffe was to them, although she terrified me!

Children with thalassemia on Lucas needing transfusions, counting the drops. One night we boiled the teats for bottle feeds – they were ruined – the wrath of Sister Lucas!

Patients having arterial transfusions – the transfusion had to be very high up and must not run through. Patients having dialysis – on a medical ward! That was scary.

Black moments

My first ward, Abernethy. I am seventeen and dressing a fungating breast cancer with exposed bone. I have never forgotten Mrs T.

How organised we were, daily duties passed on from grade to grade, always a hand-written report after nights off. All that pioneering work,

Saint Bartholomew's Hospital.
London. E.C.1.

TELEPHONE MONARCH 7777
TELEGRAPHIC ADDRESS
"RAHERE," CENT LONDON

15th January, 1965

Dear Miss Berry,

I am writing to tell you that arrangements are being made to receive you at the Preliminary Training School on Monday 8th February, 1965. Your address while you are there will be Piggott's Manor, Letchmore Heath, Near Watford, Herts. *Subject to a satisfactory X-ray report after 21st January.

Trains go from St.Pancras to Radlett, and you should arrange to arrive at Radlett Station between the hours of 2 and 3 p.m. A car will meet those trains to convey Student Nurses to the house.

You should bring the following with you to the Preliminary Training School:-

Birth Certificate.
Medical Card.
Stamped National Insurance Card.
Umbrella, clearly marked with name.
Gym dress, or shorts and a blouse, or something suitable for P.T.

If you do not possess a Medical Card and National Insurance Card, will you please obtain them from your local office of the Ministry of National Insurance before your entry, in order to avoid much waste of time during the Course.

I will now order your uniform and you will find it awaiting you at the Preliminary Training School.

You will be required to purchase two pairs of the regulation uniform shoes. If you have not already been measured and fitted for these at the Shoe Fitting Service here, arrangements will be made for you to have this done after you enter the Preliminary Training School. In the meantime, will you please bring with you one pair of suitable shoes, preferably black lace with flat heels, or brown if this is not possible. In addition, you will need black stockings, which may also be purchased through the Shoe Fitting Service. If you have not been measured for your shoes as above, you may purchase black stockings from the Hospital Shoe Fitter when you come up.

If you are sending a trunk in advance, to avoid delay, please address as follows: Preliminary Training School, Piggott's Manor, St.Bartholomew's Hospital, Letchmore Heath, Via Radlett Station, Herts.

Yours sincerely,

T. H. Loveridge

Matron and Superintendent of Nursing.

Joining instructions for entry to PTS Anne Berry's letter detailing the arrangements made for her entry to Preliminary Training School, Piggott's Manor.

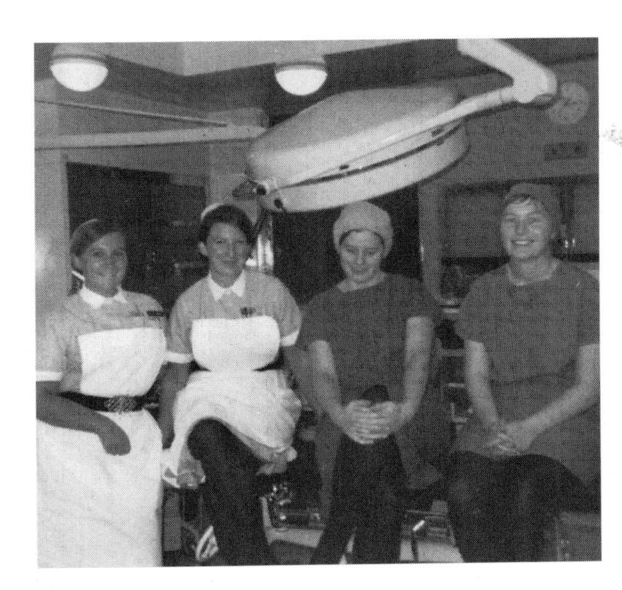

In an operating theatre
L-R: Anne Berry, Jean Gaunt and two operating theatre nurses.

children with sickle cell anaemia, retinoblastoma, putting in shunts for hydrocephalous. Frightening transfusions of cytotoxic drugs, peritoneal dialysis etc. We worked with such eminent doctors and usually took it all in our stride.

The fun side

Did we really stand in the fountain on Christmas Day? Carol singing while wearing our cloaks inside out.

Going to Oxford Street after night duty – falling asleep over coffee in Dickens and Jones – taxi back.

"Bart's Nurses' Home please."

"Okay love, no charge!"

I recall all of my dear friends, but especially Gill. I remember Simon Harris telling me that he was with Danny when he met Gill for the first time. Simon was furious that "Danny got the pretty one."

And yet, we found time to make sandwiches on Sundays, individual boiled eggs, cups of tea on demand, talking to patients and relatives, giving them our undivided attention. All of this sadly no longer a nurse's role and rarely seen nowadays.

Yes I loved my time at Bart's and it gave me good friends, a career, my husband and family!

A Houseman's Tale by Anne Berry

Some people say a Houseman's life
is full of stress and strain.
With night nurse woes, your sleep soon goes –
and it's morning once again.
You're on the ward 8.30 sharp,
You've done the round by 10.
If you don't get a breather soon, you'll go
quite round the bend!

There are drugs to board and forms to sign.
A patient or four to clerk.
They want you to take a duty case – but
you're going to stop that lark.
The list is long, and now it's late –
the hernia will have to go.
You'd better check, that blood's due through
and it's going rather slow.

They haven't found those X-rays yet
The Professor won't be happy.
There is time to get them instead of lunch,
But you'd better make it snappy.
By 6 o'clock there's peace at last and your
thirst is quite alarming.
So nip out smart
To the Old White Hart
The barmaid there is charming.

Back by 8, you've got quite a date –
There's a visitor angrily storming.
Demanding to know why her 'dear' husband
Joe is discharged without giving her warning.
Phew – got rid of her
But now you must stir and write up the
Night sedation.
Or else you'll be rung
At quarter to one
By the Night Nurse Corporation.

No time to eat.
No time to think.
The questions come thick and fast.
Just how are you going to last?
But don't despair
Or pull out your hair.
Sit down and drink your caffeine.
And then if you could
Would you be so good
As to come and check this morphine!

Jan Bramley

Interview

I cannot remember the various parts of the day in detail but I do recall the interview with Miss Coker. I felt that she really challenged each answer I'd given and remember walking out at the end feeling drained and thinking it would be remarkable if I was offered a place! I'd had interviews at Guy's and Tommy's, which had been very easy and laid back and maybe I accepted the place at Bart's partly because of that feeling…?

Worst Memories

I did night duty towards the end of our first year with just a few members of our Set. Most of you had all done it earlier as ward juniors. My worst memory was standing outside Miss Roe's office feeling very inexperienced and waiting to see where I would be sent to 'extra'. Even if I was just to be a 'stand in' night junior or an 'extra', it meant a different, unknown ward most nights. By that time in our training I had only done three-month spells on two wards.

Horror of horrors, occasionally I had to 'special.' One night I was sent to W. G. Grace to 'special' in the recovery room. After consulting the night sister, the night staff nurse (how I loved her) arranged for me to be the junior, whilst her permanent night junior – a striped belt – went into the recovery room! I really hated those three months on night duty.

The other worst memories were finding Sister Bowlby difficult to please, which probably goes for a good number of the Set and quite a feisty run-in with Sister Kenton.

Again on night duty, but this time as a staff nurse, she loudly tore strips off me one morning for having removed some waterproof sheeting that was protecting cotton sheets on a babies cot (I can't remember why they should have been there). I was 100% certain the sheeting had not been there when I went on duty and quite out of character for me in those days, I ended up standing up for myself and shouting back. In the next

End of third year 'White Belts' L–R: Penny Farrant, Stephanie Norbury, Wendy Williams, Chris Bailey and Jan Bramley. Note the short skirts!

baby's cubicle the junior sister's eyes nearly popped out of her head! After a few tears in the sluice I went and gave the report after which Sister Kenton took me into her sitting room and smoothed things over. She wanted to cancel my appointment half an hour later with Miss Harper to have my staffing reports read. Despite being quite upset by it all I rather stubbornly and ungraciously insisted on keeping the appointment, but to this day I can't really remember much about the reports!

Best Memories

Good memories of Bart's completely annihilate any bad memories and looking back, I think for me, it was one of the really happy times of my life. I learnt so much in those four years. I loved all my times on the wards, especially doing the obstetric course and my time as a staff nurse on Paget, where I did a longer period than usual as Sister Paget had to do some night duty and I stayed on as staff nurse whilst she completed this.

The very lasting memory will be the camaraderie between members of the Set. We all had our smaller groups, but there was always a collective friendship. I'd had long-standing school friends, but especially being an only child and attending a day school, had never lived in such close contact and friendship before. Obviously with so many of us returning each time for our reunions, that feeling has remained and stood the test of time.

Funniest Memories

Getting into uniform for the first time and trying to make our caps!

On my first ward, sterilizing the thermometers and then running them under hot water to remove the solution and breaking them. Not really funny at the time, but Sister Stanmore was brilliant and restored my completely deflated self esteem by enabling me to laugh at myself as well as pointing out the cost!

I do remember laughing about things until you cried – I suppose it was such good therapy. I remember the laughter but not the sources of the hilarity – rather sad really.

Sandy Camp

Top ten memories in no particular order!

- Shelagh making our caps.
- James Gibb Ward full of lusty young men. One particularly well endowed African chap being quite pleased to see me when I went to help him out of the bath!
- Explaining to Matron that I did not know the man found in my room at Maybury. (I didn't, honest!)
- Sandra eating sausage with marmalade.
- Singing *There's a Kind of Hush* to a baby with hydrocephalus.
- Going to the folk music club.
- Matron's Ball.
- Throwing laundry bags down the corridor in the new block.
- Mrs Cannon, a lovely lady who let Geoff and I stay in her caravan on Hayling Island.
- A lady with a four-stone ovarian cyst. We had to support it in a roller towel so she could get to the loo.

St Bart's Fountain which was commissioned in 1859 Alice Colby seated in front of the fountain that she always longed to jump into but was never brave enough to do so.

Alice Colby

I have so many happy memories of Bart's and our time in London – friendships, fun, laughter, kindness, thought for each other and of course the training and work. So many new experiences and I sometimes wonder how we coped with them all at such a young age.

I think I nursed as I knew I could then travel. I have loved all my nursing and it has enabled me to support myself. I feel proud to be a nurse and I still love being kind to people and looking after them.

I remember the familiarity of Elaine's blue dress on the bed at Piggott's Manor and the relief of sharing a room. We were at school together although we did not know each other very well as I was a boarder and Elaine a day girl. Little did I know what a close friend she was to become over the years.

I think I found some of the teaching at Piggott's Manor rather unreal and longed to be on the wards with real people. It was a fun time though! Trying to fold those caps…!

My first ward was Lawrence, with Sarah. We were told that it was a women's surgical ward. Imagine our delight when we discovered it was full of men! I don't think I noticed at first but Sarah did!

Alice Colby Alice relaxing in her room.

A girls' night in
L–R: Anne Runciman, Lynn Grainger and Alice Colby.

Sister Lawrence was a wonderful lady. She sent me to the kitchen to make scones for the patients and also entrusted me with her niece who I took to Battersea Fun Fair and various other places in London. Very brave as having lived in Suffolk I had only crossed London on my way to school. Sarah and I laughed so much – it was a wonderful start to nursing and I have pondered as to why such a remarkable lady as Sister Lawrence should die in a road accident. Thanks to her I never overfill tea cups!

I remember people jumping into the fountain after a Ball but I don't think I was brave enough to do so although I longed to.

Set Rep meetings…

Thank you all for everything and our wonderful friendships.

Irene Collings

I do have many happy memories of my time at Bart's. I loved the camaraderie and chatting in each other's rooms after we had come off duty. If we had concerns it was so much easier to share them with our friends.

I enjoyed all the wards I worked on but Kenton Ward has always been special to me. The children, in spite of some awful illnesses, kept remarkably happy and quite cheeky. I remember one time on night duty when we put the lights on in the morning, I was singing along to the radio when the little boy I was washing told me I was the only person he'd heard who sang worse than his dad. It certainly made us all laugh.

Irene Collings and Mary-Anne De Vere.

When one of the long staying children had a birthday, there would be a little tea party in Sister's sitting room for them and quite often Miss Loveridge would also attend. One little boy I was particularly fond of was allowed to come back to our flat for afternoon tea. I don't think that would be allowed today!

Elaine Fullard

I was doing fine in my interview until I was absolutely floored by Matron's question, "Do you help your mother with the dusting?" At the time, I spent most of my spare time careering about the woods on horse-back, so was dumbfounded! However, I did recover and quoted our childhood 'Helping Mother' rota of *Set and Dry, Clear and Put Away, Household I and Household II* that I shared with my brothers and sister. That must have saved the day, since I spent many hours after that damp dusting the bedside lockers.

I vividly remember arriving at Piggott's Manor and being so delighted to see Alice's clothes in the bedroom we were to share as we had been at school together. I felt, too, that it was like a conversion when I was told to wash off my make up, and my hair was scraped back and a tight white, stiffly starched cap was safety-pinned on. I sat at our first teatime with the safety pin sticking into my neck.

The sight and smell of my first day on the wards will last with me forever too. I had the kind companionship of Ann Stringfellow and the gentle care of the plump Sister Colston, but I was still shocked rigid by the sight of a lady sitting up in the bed by the door looking quite healthy but who was bright *yellow* (with jaundice as I later found out). Too much for a girl who had just galloped around the Chiltern Hills for her teenage years. We had learned the elements of ward protocol, one of the most important being never put red and white flowers together as it is a superstition of imminent death… I never, ever put red and white flowers together even now.

I then fell into the cruel hands of Sister Rees-Mogg. I remember her cornering me in the sluice when I was exhausted and hungry after an 11-hour night shift and giving me such a dressing down, ghastly.

However, my mother had always instilled in us, that if you start anything, it's best to finish it and 'bits of paper' were necessary to get through life with, so I stuck at the Bart's career and escaped as much as I could in between shifts. I would rush off at 12.15pm on a 'split duty' and

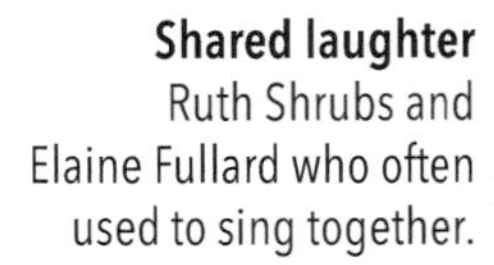

Shared laughter
Ruth Shrubs and Elaine Fullard who often used to sing together.

join the lunchtime tours of the British Museum or jump on my bicycle and cycle as far as Piccadilly Circus. I would never dare to cycle round it now, but I did in 1965. I used my bike for travelling from Maybury Mansions in West London to Bart's, and one night, as I was in Holborn nearing Bart's, a policeman stopped me to ask, did I know that I hadn't got my cycle lights on? I replied no, and that I was a nurse going on duty. He then promptly said, "I'll switch them on for you!"

I remember the warmth of the friendships among our Set, how I took over at 7.30am from Sarah and Alice who had queued since 4.30am at Covent Garden to get tickets at £5 each to see Rudolf Nureyev and Margot Fonteyn dance together in *Romeo and Juliet*, a wonderful experience.

My happiest days on the wards came when I was recovering either from a torn back muscle (having heaved a fifteen-stone man out of the bath) or getting a bad dose of glandular fever (which I'd contracted from kissing a gorgeous medical student while I was in Sick Rooms) I can't remember. Anyway, I couldn't do any tough physical work so I was sent round by the dustbins at the back of Bart's to the VD Clinic! There, I was part of a small friendly team who dealt with the motley assortment of patients who crept in. I was so happy there that I presented Sister VD with a bunch of Dutch tulips that I'd brought back from an adventurous weekend in Holland. She looked at them quizzically, asked tentatively, "Do you think that they are clean?" (that, in relation to the horrific bugs that were being identified in our clinics, was an odd question), but they were allowed to grace our little 'shangri-la' of fun and informality in our clinic.

Qualified nurses at Prizegiving Back L–R: Sarah Johnson, Alice Colby, Liz Senter, Elaine Fullard and Ruth Shrubbs. Front L–R: Lynn Grainger and Anne Thomas.

Another hidden away treasure near the VD clinic was the private ward, perhaps others will be able to remember what it was called. Anyway, there I remember nursing the mother of the infamous Kray twins. She could not have been more gentle, generous and loving towards us. I recall that she shared her enormous box of *Melting Moments* with us. These sweets were brightly coloured and had soft jelly insides. Her presence was very 'hush-hush'. Mrs Kray was recovering from a cholecystectomy.

There are so many more jumbled memories. Inside the hospital there was the incident of when I had meticulously laid up a trolley for the houseman to stitch up a Smithfield Market porter's scalp in one of the green tiled side rooms in the Outpatient's department. It was about 3.30am and because he had imbibed a bit too much alcohol, there was a strong smell of it as he sweated it out. A policeman with whom we often shared tea, toast and jam in the wee hours, had expressed a wish to see the stitching up procedure. He was tall and straight in his dark uniform, but all too soon he had fainted right across my immaculate trolley at the sight of blood!

I, as a naive young girl, came face-to-face with the domestic violence of our patients from Islington and the East End of London. I was horrified to have to help a lady who looked like a pin cushion after having been attacked by her husband with a sharp pair of scissors.

Another memorable incident was having to escort a dental patient, who was losing a lot of blood from a mouth injury, in an ambulance with the siren on full blast, and speeding round the corner of Oxford Circus and Regent's Street. The anxiety still comes back to me even now when I emerge from the Underground station.

I had my own remarkable experience in an operating theatre where a patient, who was conscious, had a burr hole made in his scalp (that was with a trephine, used since Roman times) and amazingly his tremors stopped immediately. I didn't really understand the science behind it, but I remember the, to me, magical effect.

Outside the world of the hospital, but only just, we were offered free passes to go and sit in the Old Bailey nearby and watch as the criminals who were sometimes sent down for life for the most appalling crimes. Also nearby in the Nurses' Home we could be served breakfast in bed on our days off. If we were going on duty and there were letters from home in our pigeon holes, we often tucked them unopened in the bib of our aprons until coffee break.

That's it, the best thing from Bart's are the lovely, life-long friends that I've made there!

Liz Goodchild

The story for me starts on the train to London and onto Piggott's Manor. Di Martin and I travelled from Nottingham together and unbeknown to us at the time Jan Bramley was also on the train. Jan was carrying an umbrella which should have been a clue. Di had been working at Boots, where my aunt also worked. When my aunt discovered from Di that she was leaving Boots to start her nursing training at Bart's she realised we would be together, so introduced us a few days before so we were able to travel together. This was a great advantage for us both and was the beginning of a very special friendship.

My first ward was Harvey, which then was a haematology ward where Sir Ronald Bodley Scott was the consultant with Dr Gordon Hamilton-Fairley, who was later blown up by the IRA. The ward was filled up with young men with leukaemia and Hodgkin's Disease and I remember walking in Oxford Street looking at all the young men and thinking they would be patients before long. Despite the sadness of the ward I loved it and I think my subsequent love of palliative care probably stems from that time.

My first year nights were spent on Harmsworth and it seemed to me then that Sister Harmsworth's main interest, when she came on duty in the morning, was not the welfare of her patients but the shine on the stainless steel bedpans. The two night nurses were expected to wash all the patients and make the beds before 7.30am so we had to start waking the patients up at 5am to get it all done. We always had to keep one eye on the door of the ward to check Night Sister didn't pay us an unscheduled visit.

Our night duty pattern was to work eight nights and then have four nights off. This gave me long enough to go home to Nottingham, so after finishing work at 8am I would travel over to St Pancras for the train. One time when I was doing the journey I slept through Nottingham and woke up at Sheffield. So on subsequent journeys I would ask someone in the carriage if they would wake me up for Nottingham. I

Student nurses at PTS Back L–R: Katie Lees, Maggie Powell, Anne Thomas and Mary Tuckwell. Front L–R: Liz Goodchild, Sandra Whitehouse and Di Martin.

also remember getting into a bath after night duty and waking up later in cold water.

I didn't like my stint on theatres much because for me patients are the most important part of nursing and in theatre they were more like inanimate objects. However I worked on the specialist theatre unit and remember being in awe of the amazing skill of the neuro and the cardiac surgeons. How life has moved on when I think now that Ronnie, my husband, has four stents in his heart which all those years ago would have involved complex surgery and taken several hours.

My head is full of little pictures

- My ongoing struggle with making our caps, which fortunately didn't need to be changed very often, so I could usually find someone to make me a new one when mine looked grubby round the edges.
- Matron, Miss Loveridge, coming down the ward with her hat billowing out behind her.
- The annual ball at the Grosvenor House where we all had to wear long gloves to shake hands with Matron and the Dean of the Medical School at the bottom of the stairs. I was sure I would trip on my dress and land in a heap at the bottom!
- My parents and Richard, my then fiancé, coming to Smithfield, where I did my staffing on View Day and meeting a much loved patient, Mr Phillips, who had an ear trumpet.

However what has stayed with me and will always be with me is the warmth of the love and friendship we as a Set share after our training together which is so wonderfully demonstrated at our reunions.

Lynn Grainger

So many memories to recall…

That first day at King's Cross picking out others on the platform carrying black umbrellas, all so terribly anxious.

Piggott's – which I loved, particularly the enormous portions of pineapple meringue which appeared weekly, I think on a Friday. We were hugely overfed.

In week one, the first chore in the group I was in was to clean the toilets before breakfast, and not being allowed to eat breakfast until they were inspected. It has had the lasting effect of making me obsessed with clean toilets!

Then there was my first ward, Fleet Street men's surgical, with Sandra, and being in utter awe of Sister Morgan but she taught us so much. Sandra of course reminded me of that terrible incident with my first suture removal. He was a Mediterranean skinned chap – very nice – and must have watched me for ages sorting out the sterile pack with all those instruments in a line on the little cloth. So there I was petrified – removal of scrotal sutures! I can remember thinking to myself I mustn't fumble around, just get on with it quickly, so made brave start and tried so hard not to be embarrassed. I can't remember how far I'd got when things started moving and the bloke very apologetically said, "I am very sorry". My heart was pounding, I looked at him, he was so embarrassed. In a very small voice, I said I needed to get something and dived out of the curtains. Sandra continues the story… (see page 96).

On a less nerve-wracking note, there were the tedious weekend cleaning jobs – bedpans 'til they shone, but worst of all dusting hundreds of Venetian blinds. I haven't had one in my own home since.

Night duty on Harvey was my small moment of glory – a very busy men's medical ward and for some reason I was the senior nurse, second year with a grey belt junior. There was a chap in the first bed who I think had had myocardial infarction but had been in the ward for ages. Instead of sleeping all night, this particular night he thrashed around the bed.

Outside Kenton Ward
Sylvia Bennett and
Lynn Grainger.

I became more anxious, got the grey belt to fetch the crash box and rang the SHO.

"What do you mean you think he's going to have heart attack? I'll come in a minute."

I could hear the laughter in their canteen. She appeared, got him all wired up and lo and behold at that very point he went into ventricular fibrillation.

I found the children's ward the most harrowing for obvious reasons and can't say I really enjoyed it. I do recall the day Sister Lucas asked me to take a curly red headed, eight-year-old epileptic girl out into the square for fresh air. She climbed one of the lamp posts and the worst happened. Not my finest moment but she was okay.

Although I lived a half hour drive from London, I recall the extraordinary freedom, wandering along the Embankment in the sunshine, feeling part of 'the big city', the riverside pubs which I didn't know existed, sunbathing in Regent's Park from Maybury, free theatre tickets, trips to the Serpentine, and those exciting Dorchester Hotel Summer Balls. Because of my closeness to home I was able to take friends, who lived further afield, home on days off or for weekends. My parents loved it and became to understand why I so enjoyed Bart's.

I was terrified in our final practical exams, somehow we came through. Staffing taught us how to manage the ward, and then the badges! I loved Bart's, it felt like a second home, taught us so many life skills, and provided lifelong friendships, but also for the first time in my life I met less advantaged people from the City of London. My parents hadn't wanted me to nurse, they thought university the place, and so first I tried physiotherapy at the London Hospital, it seemed 'one up' on nursing, but I am so very glad I changed. I returned to Bart's as Sister Pink on ITU after six months midwifery in Plymouth. It was challenging but wasn't the same as those wonderful student days. I left after four months to marry the naval officer I had met in Plymouth.

Gill Hayward

Growing up I had three main ambitions – to attend a Buckingham Palace Garden Party, attend a Cambridge May Ball and marry a doctor! The first I did with my parents at sixteen and the second at nineteen.

I did a secretarial diploma with languages and was working in the city but was not meeting enough eligible men! I had a friend who was a student radiographer at Bart's so on a whim I applied for nursing at Bart's. I was interviewed very quickly by a very smiley matron to whom nothing seemed to be a problem. I had no sciences but was offered a place for the following February. I worked where I was until January then started at PTS.

I had been living in a flat so it was quite a shock. I arrived wearing nail polish and lipstick which I was quickly told to remove. I muttered to my mother that I had not thought this was a convent. She told my father to expect me home within the week!

We had a lot of fun and made lasting friends though. I wheeled a trolley of china from the dining room, some china jumped off with a crash and I laughed. Miss Ebdon questioned whether I thought I was serious enough for nursing. This question arose again after my blanket bathing of Angelina. Angelina was the large Bakelite mannequin who was used for practising on. Flowers jumped off trolleys on my first ward so it was decided not to take the flowers out, at least when I was the junior on duty. I also recall being thrown in the fountain, in full uniform, by a group of medical students, on Christmas day...

I met my husband on my second ward though it was to be some time before we married.

I have a note from a patient who could not talk very well, saying how much pleasure my smile gave her and never to lose it.

I was on my first lot of nights, on Bowlby, when invited to a surgical firm party. Night Sister Jane said I could go and she would send a replacement, but Sister Bowlby would have none of it. Night Sister said that this was most unfair to my partner so sent a staff nurse so Sister

Bowlby could not refuse, though she did not forgive me. However my partner was Danny and I was worried that he might find someone else if I wasn't there! I remember ringing to say I felt unwell so would not be on duty that night when we had gone to a wedding. You could hear trains in the background!

Though I did nursing for very odd reasons, I have loved it and our training gave me so much confidence. I have worked almost continuously. There was always work wherever we moved to. I was offered a Research Sister Post in Oxford which I did until my eldest daughter was born. When Danny was doing research and we had two children, they formed a Nurse Bank in Oxford and, to begin with, you could work for any hours on your chosen speciality and there was always work for my chosen hours. I then did Family Planning and then Practice Nursing since 1987 and now I am finishing off summarising the notes. I have worked for various consultants both nursing and secretarial duties. It really has combined well with family life and I feel very lucky though I am going to have to let go very soon. Still, I am very fortunate with the grandchildren and five live nearby, and my daughters work!

Postscript from her husband, Danny

Gill died in October 2011, having written this contribution the previous year. I still miss her greatly. She was the driving force in our marriage, but I count myself lucky to have enjoyed forty-four years with her and her sparkling eyes. I now have fourteen grandchildren ranging from two to eighteen years old, and they have become my raison d'être.

Sarah Johnson

As long as I can remember I had wanted to be a nurse. Bart's was my only hospital of choice, partly because of local connections. This was confirmed when I was a patient at the age of fifteen, for a procedure to flatten bat ears. Thank you Paget Ward and the NHS; I was left with wondrous thoughts of administering angels, and without this operation my ears could have been mistaken for wings.

I remember little of the interview apart from meeting Lizzie Senter and her mother, but what must have impressed the interviewer was the olive green suit, with matching wool hat of course, (probably chosen by my mother who had not attended a 'Colour Me Beautiful' session at her WI).

The first of the Set I met on the way to PTS at St Pancras station were Adrea and Mary, then, on arrival Sue Shouler and Chris Nobes with whom I was to share a bedroom. The layout is still clear in my mind with pinky red candlestick bedspreads.

The uniform dress shrunk so much I had to get replacements, or was it the food? The black shoes did eventually soften but it was always a relief to change into tennis plimsolls.

Going to 'work' at Piggott's Manor was so exciting with the mock ward where we learnt bandaging and laying up trolleys and could even play at being patients. The classroom with desks in rows meant concentrating on nursing theory; the dreaded weekly tests on Fridays were never my greatest moments.

I was too young to appreciate the lovely gardens; if rose pruning had been in the syllabus it would have been an additional useful skill for later life.

The social life revolved around sitting drinking coffee with new friends, playing tennis as well as the odd visit to the local pub, where we started eyeing up the trainees from the flying school before moving on to medical students. What a change from boarding school!

White Belt study block The February 1965 Set in the classroom where they studied nursing theory. The tutor at the back is Winifred Hector.

Memories of Queen Mary's Nurses' Home

- Each other's rooms became centres of companionship, sharing experiences with shoulders to laugh and cry on and, in retrospect, the rather worrying sessions with an Ouija board.
- The twenty-four-hour sound of the bedpan washers in the ward sluices which backed on to our rooms.
- The large gracious sitting room with its grand piano waiting to be played.
- The quiet formal library.
- The swimming pool in the basement of Gloucester House.
- The rigmarole of late passes.
- 'Hops' in the hall where, on one occasion, Alice and I had to make a hasty getaway running through the underpass to safety.
- The highlight of the year was Matron's Ball and weeks before, medical students would be flaunting themselves for an invitation.

Newly qualified Pictured by the fountain. L–R: Liz Senter, Alice Colby, Sarah Johnson and Anne Thomas. Note the stiffly starched aprons.

Moving to Maybury Mansions meant the dread of oversleeping or overrunning shifts thus missing the coach, so uniform or mufti was in the wrong place. Shifts beginning at lunchtime often involved walking part of the way to Bart's and stopping in Oxford Street where buying materials at John Lewis kept my sewing machine very busy. One treat was ordering breakfast in bed but the anticipation was better than what arrived. We made much use of free theatre tickets and played tennis even after night duty, but so often hours were spent idly chatting in each other's rooms.

What freedom to move to Islington after qualifying; the house I was in belonged to an Australian artist/sculptor who left some dubious artwork around; there was a garden, a grand piano in the sitting room, a basement perfect for parties and the hall big enough for the bicycles. Cycling to Bart's in the early morning was memorable, going through Smithfield meat market with all the gruesome hunks of meat with accompanying wolf whistles from the cheery porters. After cycling home after an early shift we often rewarded ourselves with fresh bread with jam. The seven of us did have a very action packed social life, which did become a little complicated at times!

As for the nursing, Lawrence was my first ward, with Alice, where Sister George-Davis ruled with a rod of iron but she taught us nursing skills never to be forgotten, from opening the envelopes of patients' post to considering whether scrambled egg would be a more appropriate alternative to the provided meal, and *never* leaving a drop of gravy or custard on the edge of the plate. I learnt how the locker round was an important social skill, how bed wheels had to point in the right direction, and how an elbow-to-hand measure was necessary for the amount of sheet tucked over the counterpane. Did the consultants really notice these details on their hallowed ward rounds? The afternoon report was always a teaching session before the bed baths. One bed bath I will never forget was when Miss Shorthouse assessed my effort on some unfortunate patient, it took so long that it was impossible to keep the water warm.

Thoughts on some other placements

- Lucas Ward terrified me with patients too tiny to touch and cockroaches so big that we almost tripped over them on night duty.
- Smithfield, where skin treatments took half a morning and the content of sputum pots had to be analysed and weighed at the end of a night.
- Radcliffe, the eye ward, where patients had to lie still for days.
- W. G. Grace where the behaviour of patients was unpredictable, giving of mag.sulph enemas pre-op and the intensive care area opposite the desk often meant nursing post-ops in iced sheets.
- Harley, where I shall never forget a young German girl who procured an abortion with a knitting needle and ended up on dialysis.
- Annie Zunz where I encountered stick-like girls with anorexia.
- Women's outpatients where the fiercesome Metty ruled, and Mr. Howkins and his retinue brought on the blushes.
- Martha's where there were always nappies to fold if there was a dearth of deliveries.
- Theatre G as a student, then a 'belt', where the steam from the boilers convinced me to get contact lenses, and maintaining the cupboard of instruments became my pride and joy. Circumcisions

and haemorrhoidectomies were far too off-putting to watch, but Mr Nash's spina bifida and Mr Griffith's big gut surgery were totally absorbing.

- My last ward, Lawrence, which was also my first, gave me my favourite few months of the four years at Bart's convincing me of my preference for surgical nursing.

It is probably true that one only remembers the good times but those four years at Bart's with the February 1965 Set were so special. Every so often I look at the patchwork quilt I made during those years and remember many of you from fragments of fabrics. One day you will have to come to identify your old clothes!

Jackie McDevitt

My memories of training at St Bartholomew's Hospital, 1965 to 1968, are a mix of highs and lows, funny and sad, but times and experiences that would prepare us for anything in our future lives.

My parents were GPs but I wanted to be a vet. I decided on nursing but I was only going to train at the best, which I did.

The only memory of the interview process which was led by Matron, Deputy Matron and Mrs Bodley Scott, was being asked to climb on and off a chair to close a window for some reason. A window which could only be conquered by using a long pole. Apparently my height was very satisfactory for the task!

I had interviews at Guy's and St Thomas' which were quite frightening but luckily I opted for Bart's and on February 8th 1965 commenced my journey into the unknown at the Preliminary Training School in Hertfordshire. I was allocated to Piggott's Manor, a lovely country mansion. My room-mate was Gill Hayward, and remember well those who had nearby rooms. My great friend Cecy Thoday quickly became the chief milliner and regular happy sessions were held at all hours with *Concrete and Clay* being the 'in' song. I still have the record. I was very particular about a well presented starch cap, but I never mastered the art of the tails and where to put the safety pin. It was here that memories began and friendships were forged; visiting others' homes at weekends and driving down to Cornwall in my parents' Austin A35 with Anne and Sandy plus various dogs crammed in for good measure. Holidays were also later taken abroad, Yugoslavia and Tenerife to name a couple. Very carefree before the real tasks commenced.

Piggott's was very near to a pilots' training school and a lovely local pub. Gill and I were at the front of the manor with a big bay window adjacent to another bay window housing one of the tutors. One evening a convoy of sports cars drove across the front lawns ejecting handsome would-be pilots who were to be seen climbing the drain pipes to gain entry. To the horror of Gill, myself and several others we looked out of our window to see the tutor looking out as well. Hardly surprising with all the noise outside. We and several others were subsequently in a lot of trouble, banned from socialising with the culprits and banned from the pub. Doors were well and truly locked at 10pm! I think we could have worked around it.

After three months we started our training for real at Bart's. Here we would not only have the wonderful training to be excellent practitioners but also respect and discipline which was entrenched into life at Bart's. As learned at PTS all beds had to be made in a certain manner, with the open end of pillows facing away from the door and bed wheels to be in alignment, especially before ward rounds. Our black cloaks were only allowed to be worn outside the wards, in the long cold corridors and en-route to our residencies. No cardigans. If on the very odd time we were spoken to by a Sister we had to remove our cloak. In the large dining room we had to sit in the row allocated to our year and never spoke to anyone in a Set above us. Sisters were always seated out of sight. Uniforms were done at the laundry and the starched aprons were never worn outdoors. Tights were black and shoes were black lace-ups if I remember. Very early on Mrs Bodley Scott saw me bending over on a ward and told me that my uniform was too short as she could see the back of my knees.

My first placement was on Stanmore, a male medical ward. We were about to encounter some lovely ward Sisters and those who were very frightening to say the least. All Sisters were known only by their ward names and we never knew their real names. Sister Stanmore veered towards the latter category, but the knowledge, skills and respect she imparted was invaluable.

I remember well the incident of Anne Runciman and myself in the sluice of Stanmore trying to remove a wasp from my bra. Anne was busy trying to undress me in order to remove it whilst not making a noise. We were paralytic with laughter but knew that Sister was probably not far away. Very funny.

Another memorable incident was just before a coffee break. If you were late for your break that was your fault. The Nightingale wards were divided into two long areas with Sister's desk situated just inside the main door so that she could peer down either side. I was taking a wash bowl full of warm water to a patient when I slipped, fell on my bottom with the water going everywhere and soaking me. I was mortified as the men were clapping, whistling and trying not to laugh which finished with booing as Sister Stanmore peered around from her desk saying,

Stanmore Ward Liz West-Watson and Jackie McDevitt looking angelic, with a patient.

"Your break has not started yet nurse". She conceded defeat and, when I got up, told me to take down another bowl and go for my break. By the time I had gone back to the Nurses' Home and changed, my break time was over!

My first surgical night duty was the female ward, Harmsworth. Sister Harmsworth was very pleasant but attention to detail was paramount. I went back to my room after a shift when the day staff nurse arrived and summoned me back to the ward. I duly complied to be met by Sister who escorted me to the sluice. During her early ward inspection she had found that the bedpans in the sluice (housed in wooden rack) were 'out of alignment'. It was the job of the lowly student nurse to leave the sluice in perfect condition on her ward. I was somewhat paranoid in the sluice for some time after this.

Another memory was on my second year night duty on Luke, the female haematology ward. Sister Luke was one of the nicest, most kind and well respected Sisters. This was a very challenging ward due to its

A view across London
Jackie McDevitt looking from the balcony of Queen Mary's Nurses' Home towards St Paul's Cathedral.

speciality. She taught me a lot. The Staff Nurse and myself were illicitly drinking coffee at the desk in the semi dark around 1am when to our horror we saw in the mirror above the desk Sister Roe, the awesome Night Sister coming out of the opposite ward. She was *early*. She was very small and used to glide along in her navy uniform, cloak and long flowing cap taking hostages along the way. We had no time but to jam the coffee mugs into the desk drawer. She wafted in, saying nothing as she obviously noticed the steam coming from the partially opened drawer. She sat down, raised her knee up to the drawer banging it and spilling the hidden coffee all over the paperwork rendering it brown and soggy. Her comment was to explain to Sister Luke why the paperwork had become illegible. Instead of asking Staff Nurse to list all the patients' names and diagnoses from memory, which was the ritual for on average thirty patients, the task was passed to me. I was a wreck, but Staff Nurse said she would own up to the soggy paperwork in the morning. I later found out that these two Sisters were great friends.

Later in this night duty Sister Roe made me do a pile of washing up in the kitchen without making a sound as she could hear me down the corridor. No wonder I hate washing up to this day! She loved me really!

A friendly porter
George, one of the porters, with Jean Gaunt and Jackie McDevitt, in 1968.

There were many happy memories as well, especially in my theatre placement which I thoroughly enjoyed but was useless. Wish I had done it later in my training.

I remember shaking with fright when I was allocated to the children's ward where Sister Kenton ruled with an iron rod. Actually it was in my third year and I was able to cope with it. I believe others did not fare so well.

I remember the mice running around the wards, as Liz Senter does, with the odd cockroach thrown in. Also the climbing in and around the gates after curfew time if we did not have a late pass. It was advisable to make friends with the night porters on the gates but I think that George put in a good word for us at times.

We explored the sights of London, had fun down Cheapside replicating the exploits of Harry Worth with the many large glass shop windows, with Jean, Anne Berry and others. I loved Pimlico, the markets, the music. It was the 60s. We had an amazing hen party for Cecy, doing Battersea fun fair, sitting in the rear carriages of the Big Dipper and the Wall of Death; neither a good idea but such fun. A highlight was thinking of buckles when we qualified, and some of us exploring The Silver Vaults in Chancery Lane. We worked very hard and earned our prizes at the end of our years at Bart's.

Finally, I wonder where the ghost of Sister Rahere is walking now. I believe that she walked the same route for many years. Was she looking for something or someone? I presume that she can no longer walk the corridor through Queen Mary's Nurses' Home to her ward, sometimes brushing lightly against you. Sometimes she used the big lift with the heavy concertina doors. She made sure that the noise of the doors was minimal, but she was there. Several of us felt her presence. She never bothered us, she never frightened us, but she was there. I think her paths are no longer there, but where is she? Perhaps her work as she knew it is done. Who knows?

Shelagh Malone

I had always wanted to be a nurse from as far back as I can remember. I don't know why as I was not following any family tradition as far as I know. So when I still had a few more years at school my uncle decided to list all the best teaching hospitals for me, and I chose Bart's. Then when my GP told me that he had trained there and would support my application my fate was sealed.

My mother came with me to the interview which I do not remember much about, but I do remember the medical, having to stand on a towel, and having my feet measured for black lace-up shoes.

I was on holiday in Torquay when I heard that my application had been accepted and felt very excited by it.

Then it was PTS and Aldenham Cottage. What an assortment of girls from all over but I was lucky to share an upstairs room with Sandy, Anne and Rosemary and we all got on well.

Each day started with kneeling for prayers before breakfast. We had uniform day when we had to make those hats which fortunately I managed to pick up pretty quickly, but I was not so keen on cleaning the toilets until my Dad gave me a few fatherly words of advice and explained the importance of doing this. Then there was more cleaning and having to wash the cloths out immediately afterwards which I still find myself doing to this day.

My parents thought it would be better for me not to go home the first weekend or I might not want to go back but, although I felt lonely it was good for me as I got to know other new people like Jo and Katie.

We all soon settled down to the routine and I remember Alice organising a tennis tournament at Piggott's Manor which I really enjoyed as I loved tennis.

Our first visit to a ward was a daunting experience but I had Beth Allen with me and her friendly manner and sense of humour kept some of the nervousness away. Heath Harrison was our ward so fluid charts were our life and we spent many happy times in the sluice together. We got to know the patients quite well as they were mostly long term and we had lots of presents when we left.

My second ward was Stanmore which I did with Liz Woodger (Woody) where the Sister made marmalade in the kitchen. Mind you we did learn a lot about nursing as she was very keen to teach us. She made us stand and watch a patient who was bleeding internally following a liver biopsy so that we would always remember what somebody looked like when they were haemorrhaging.

Night duty on Mary was an experience, being paired with a scatty white belt, when we spent time making cream drinks in the kitchen and going down for tea and toast at about 5am. I seemed to be always eating even having bread and butter and cakes at tea time – I've never been slim since!

We did eventually qualify and were then allowed to move out and I remember well the flat I shared in Islington with Katie, Anne and Rosemary above a launderette. No part of the flat was on the same level but we always had a constant supply of hot water. One particular memorable event was being locked in the flat by the others when I was on night duty and the landlord having to get a ladder to get me out through a window.

After four years, which seemed to fly by, it all came to an end and we went our separate ways but still thankfully manage to meet up every five years and remember the 'good old days'.

Di Martin

Student Nurses in full uniform L–R: Katie Lees, Di Martin, Sandra Whitehouse, Mary Tuckwell and Maggie Powell.

Memories of a not very brave student nurse or, indeed, person

I've always felt that part of me nursed to please my mother but am I glad I did. My start wasn't very auspicious – the week before I'd witnessed a man fall under a bus and completely squash his hand, and then when I arrived at Smithfield I assumed all the men sitting on benches in bloody aprons were surgeons. I nearly turned tail at that point. Things got worse when on my first ward I took a lady to the loo where she had a carotid haemorrhage and died. Such awful things never happened again, and of course the wonderful friendship of you all far outweighed my fear.

As far as funny memories go I will never forget a night on Heath Harrison with a Staff Nurse called Sue who had been a nun. She'd left the convent after having a silent lunch one day when the chocolate sauce for pudding was circulated as gravy and vice versa and no-one spoke! Anyway, she wanted to cook a duck, that her father had shot, for Miss Leach (do any of you remember her), and with Night Sister turning a blind eye all went well. Would this happen now!

The nerves kicked in again when I was asked to staff on Kenton. I was absolutely terrified of her although I did admire her. This all came back to me when my daughter was nursing at Bart's and I went up for View Day and spied Sister Kenton in St Bart's the Less. I started to shake and hid behind a pillar which Anna, my daughter, reminded me of today – she says it's the only time she's had to protect me and loves to tell the story.

I do also wonder, on reflection, where were the Swinging Sixties – not very evident in Queen Mary's Nurses' Home. Do you remember the rules and regs, and not even brothers or fathers allowed in?

Did any of you see the Beatles?

I must tell you all though, that my very first visit on the district showed me I'd found my place. I'd always been told off for talking to (or even making tea for) relatives, so to feel that I was nursing the whole family was wonderful. I had thirty happy years learning from them all and wouldn't have missed it for the world.

Josephine M

I don't remember stripping at interview. I remember the prospectus said we had to be five foot two inches and I was half an inch short so I wrote and said I would stretch myself. When I finally started I saw that one of the assistant matrons, Miss Coker, was much shorter than me! I was seventeen at interview and told that I was so shy that I should try and get a job for the next year where I would meet people, so I worked at Harrods on the shop floor.

I recall sharing a room at Piggott's Manor with Chris Cooke and Gill Smedley (I think that was her name) and her saying she didn't mind which ward she was going on as long as it wasn't Bowlby. I then saw our first ward list and noticed that Bowlby was my first ward and no one would be on it with me either – what fear! I was absolutely terrified on the coach journey as we went up to Bart's each time for our ward visits. I went to below seven stone on Bowlby as I couldn't eat but did, in fact, get a good report. The tea trolley was a special memory of Bowlby as it *had* to come out at 3.25pm and woe betide you if it was wheeled out at 3.24pm or 3.26pm.

Another frightening ward was Kenton but most of the nurses had D+V whilst I was there and I managed not to succumb – Sister was so pleased with me for that. I remember being told that she only had to see an ill child to be pretty much sure what the matter was before any investigations were held. I was there for View Day and a group of us went off very early with Sister to the old Covent Garden to buy the flowers to decorate the ward.

One night a poor doctor, having been on duty all day and most of the night, asked me in the early hours to make him scrambled eggs and I had to admit I didn't know how to!

Last autumn I decided to try and find Maybury Mansions. They are now private flats called Maybury Court in Marylebone Street.

Christine Nobes

My headmistress had wanted me to apply to Tommy's which I was determined not to do as she was on the selection panel. I sent off for the prospectuses of Guy's, The Middlesex and Bart's. I applied to Bart's because they had a better swimming pool than the Middlesex, and you didn't have to write an essay which was part of the entry criteria for Guy's. I remember being asked at interview if there was anything about nursing that concerned me and replying, "Giving injections".

I was fortunate to only have to wait a few months from interview to starting which meant that I did not have to attend the intensive secretarial course which my father thought all girls should complete.

At PTS I shared a room with Sarah Johnson and Sue Shouler. I remember being very anxious on the coach journey to Bart's for our first introduction to the wards. I was on James Gibb and remember one day Sister making me return to a patient who hadn't peed sufficiently. On being offered a bottle he filled it and half a second one. Sister James Gibb instilled into me the importance of my work as a junior nurse. Her view was that a patient was more likely to speak to a nurse cleaning a locker than to a senior nurse. I remember one Sunday afternoon being aware that the oldest staff member on the ward was the staff nurse and that the wellbeing of the patients was in the trust of three of us aged between eighteen and twenty-one.

Much later during training, when on night duty on QE II theatres, a 'pump case' returned to theatre as an emergency. The registrar raced into theatre in his outdoor clothes to operate. His speed of reaction probably saved the patient's life. I loved the drama of the 'pump case' operations when on chest theatres, as we all stood waiting for the heart to recommence beating.

I lived at Maybury Mansions which I enjoyed apart from on night duty as I found sleeping a real problem, especially on Sunday when the Salvation Army played outside the National Heart Hospital.

My final ward was Bowlby, which I grew to love. Sister Bowlby was not happy that I was leaving to get married and made life difficult to begin with, but gradually mellowed. It was a very busy ward on which the patients' needs were the highest priority and very well run. Despite the workload we were rarely late off duty.

My final reminiscence is being called to Matron's office regarding a mortgage application form which, due to my salary, they couldn't complete. Once they realised that it was just a formality because the mortgage was to be in Ray's and my name they relaxed. Almost fifty-two years on we remain happily married.

Stephanie Norbury

I was a shy but excited teenager when, with my mother, I went for my interview at Bart's in 1964. I had also applied to St Thomas' and Guy's but really wanted Bart's as I had been told by a school friend's mother – who was herself a nurse – that Bart's was the greatest as well as the oldest hospital in the world. Tommy's and Guy's both felt I was too shy and that I should do some voluntary work first to see if I really was suited to nursing. Probably very wise advice. However, the Matron at Bart's liked me. She spoke to my mother too, who looked after me throughout the interview. I was full of altruism and enthusiasm for 'helping people'. Although my father was keen that I should go to either art school or to university to study English (my two favourite subjects), I wanted a career that would always be in demand so that I could travel and be able to support myself. I did not see any hope of anyone ever wanting to marry me – the usual 'career' for girls of our generation after a short working life. Teaching was not an option, I was too shy, and I wanted something better than being a secretary. Our choices were limited in those days.

At PTS I was impressed by how sophisticated all the others seemed. Of course I know now that this was hardly true, but I started, for the first time, at PTS to experiment with make-up and hair colour because the other girls were doing so, and this caused some surprise when I went home on days off. I remember Penny Farrant, who shared a room with me, seeming so assured and confident and I longed to be like that. Sandra was so beautiful and she also had a sports car – unheard of luxuries! PTS was very much like boarding school and I still felt like a school girl. I was introduced during our lectures – for the first time – to the intricacies of human anatomy and physiology, including sexual reproduction – not something that I had discussed with anyone before. It all seemed very intriguing.

I loved the wards and the patients. My first ward was Rahere, a men's medical ward and I can remember every single one of them, they were so kind to this shy junior grey-belt. Sue Dale was my fellow probationer there. On my birthday the men on my ward pooled their resources and bought me *The New World Symphony* by Dvorak on LP – which I still treasure. Patients stayed for such a long time on medical wards in those days and I got to know them all quite well. Of course, when you are nineteen, three months seems for ever.

Then on my days off I wandered round London – first the City all around us, just walking and looking at all the history. Then I discovered Oxford Street and the clothes of 'Swinging' London. I made a resolution to transform myself from a mouse into a dolly bird. I started very gradually to go to parties and longed to appear sophisticated and confident and started to pretend that I was. The make up and the hairstyles did not go down well at all with the sisters and senior nursing officers. But men started to notice me. This was heady stuff and I did not know how to handle it all. Many years later, when I worked again with Trevor Powles at the Royal Marsden near my home in Surrey, we sat down one day and had a long chat about our memories of Bart's. He told me I had been 'a breath of fresh air' and how old-fashioned it all seemed now. It was naivety, really.

I was a bit shy when I started PTS at Bart's and I had always been laughed at in school for being skinny when curvaceous girls were in fashion. But in the 1960s with Twiggy and company being the 'look of the moment', I started to enjoy the dolly bird look. Then at a Bart's party I was introduced to John Hardy Clarke, a journalist at the *Daily Express*. He told me that the Women's Fashion Editor was doing a weekly series in the paper about ordinary people and their clothes and asked if he could tell her about me. Wow, how exciting! So she invited me along to the Daily Express Office in Fleet Street one day. I had such fun that day posing while the photographer took pictures of me. You can imagine, to a young teenager it was heaven – I thought I had 'arrived'. The only trouble was, when they interviewed me, they asked about my salary and I told them I earned £16 a month. They mistook the salary for a weekly wage and wrote in the article that I earned £16 a week which would have been a lot in those days. So the whole purpose of the article was lost. I wanted to show that nurses and people who didn't earn a lot could make their own clothes and find their own style. But I have never forgotten the thrill of being a model in London for one day!

Bart's and the friends I made there, and the patients I nursed, remain dear memories to me. Nursing did not, in the end, prove to be the career for me. After degrees in Art and English and a useful secretarial course,

WOMAN'S EYE on Real Clothes for Real People by ANN RYAN

Cover-girl look . . . on nurse's pay

Off duty, Stevie's still on call for glamour

The addict

Stunning

Bargain

Research: SUE SNELL
Sketch: JIL SHIPLEY
Pictures: MICHAEL McKEOWN

A London model for a day The *Real Clothes for Real People* article from the *Daily Express* in which Stephanie Norbury, a newly qualified State Registered nurse, talked about fashion and make up, and modelled some of the latest styles.

I found my true vocation. But I don't regret my training. I would perhaps have gone even more 'off the rails' if I had just gone to university or art college straight from school. As it was, I never experimented with drugs, and the Hippy Movement was unattractive to me. And I learned not to be entirely self-indulgent and to find fulfilment in giving comfort and care to other people. And all those useful things we learnt! I can still make a bed in record time and I have irritatingly high hygiene standards, so my husband tells me, and a couple of times when I have been present at an accident or emergency, my nursing skills have instinctively come back to me in seconds and I have responded with assurance.

I am impressed by those of our Set who have continued to contribute so much to nursing. In retrospect perhaps I should have gone away and grown up a little more before starting my training. But I wouldn't have missed that exciting time, really. So that is why I love to come to the reunions. For a short time, with old friends and old memories, we are the young girls again that we used to be.

Maggie Powell

A few brief memories...

I was probably the most unprepared student nurse ever – I was so sure Bart's would be dying to have me I didn't bother to apply anywhere else! Of course I was right...

The interview was very scary – almost as scary as Mrs Stringfellow and her daughter who seemed very sophisticated and seemed to know the ins and outs of interviews – just goes to show you should never judge people by first impressions! Anyway the two other things I remember from my interview are being asked to shut the window (presumably to see if I could manage this in a ladylike manner!) and being asked in a perfect Queen's English, "Do you ride?" to which I replied, "A bicycle, not a horse", at which point my mother nearly had a heart attack! She really thought I'd blown my chance with sarcasm so nearly had another heart attack when I was *accepted*!

At PTS I shared a room with Mary and Di and we were forever getting notes from Miss Ebdon asking us to tidy it up – poor Di, it was never her mess! Imagine how the students of today would react to that – let alone learning how to polish a table! Another thing I learnt to do at PTS was how to smoke (probably due to that sophisticated Stringy again). Learning to drink came later once we discovered medical students.

Once on the wards I managed to get by without doing anything momentous or particularly noteworthy. But I often wonder how in those days we were put in charge of a ward at night when we were nineteen years old – nowadays nurses are barely allowed a glimpse of a patient until fully trained! I now pale at the thought of dealing with people returning from theatre, being the duty firm and having emergency admissions – how we didn't manage to actually kill anybody I shall never know!

Who would have thought that some memories are still as clear as if they had happened yesterday rather than fifty plus years ago?

One day whilst working as a stripe on Kenton, the lovely children's ward with a notorious martinet as Sister, at mid-morning I took the lift to

Ready for hospital L–R: Katie Lees, Di Martin, Maggie Powell and Mary Tuckwell. Di, Maggie and Mary shared a room at PTS.

go down to coffee. Who should follow me in but Sister Kenton herself. This is what followed:

S.K: "Are you going to coffee Nurse Powell?"

Me: "Yes Sister, Nurse Fox (a lovely blue belt) told me to go now while we're not too busy."

S.K. (with no hint of a smile): "That's fine, clean your shoes before you come back on duty will you."

The omission of a question mark above is deliberate – this was certainly not a question! I should add perhaps that although a stickler for discipline Sister Kenton was a brilliant children's nurse and luckily, apart from the above, I managed to steer pretty clear of her sharp tongue.

Who could ever forget the experience of first year nights – eight nights on, four nights off! I don't think any of today's students would believe our tales of the endless bed changing, constant tea making, reassuring hand holding and limitless TLC that kept us busy all night long. Although I do remember making fudge in Waring kitchen one night – surely Night Sister must have smelled it!

Then, just as we were on our last legs there was the question of how to give twenty-six patients early morning tea and then to get them washed and their beds stripped and made again (pillow ends away from the door, nurse!) by half past seven! Morning rush, like so much of our training, is currently resting in the archive file! I was on Harvey and Liz West-Watson on Heath Harrison – both notoriously busy wards – and we were always late down to breakfast, some others in our Set were often on their second cigarette before we even sat down and started our porridge!

As a fifth year in A & E, my worst nightmare was having to cover the dental clinic when they were doing extractions – they had to have a qualified nurse in attendance if administering anaesthetics and I always prayed it wouldn't be me (dentaphobia is my middle name!). When, inevitably my turn came I asked the dentist, whose name escapes me, how he could bear to do such a horrible job? With a wry grin he replied, "The only other person who has asked me that was a gynaecologist."

Far too much from me I feel, but would like to add an amusing story from about ten years ago which epitomises our rigorous training and passion for standards. We had to have my partner's mother assessed re mental capacity and the retired old-school doctor doing the assessment had originated from Tommy's. Richard was chatting away with him about this and that and happened to say, "My wife is a nurse, she trained at Bart's." We still chuckle over his reply, "Oh, you poor boy – your life must be ruled with a rod of iron!"

Adrea Ripley

A few memories hastily put together on my way to a Bart's reunion

Sitting on the train as it clattered into Blackfriars, struggling to overcome the overwhelming desire to 'stay put' and return home, instead of reporting for duty on Kenton (my second ward).

Conversely, wishing it wasn't my day off on Colston (my third ward) as I was enjoying it so much!

Arriving on Dalziel to discover that the charming Mr H, with depression, had suddenly flipped. During the afternoon he charged maniacally out of the ward, bursting through the double doors. I followed. As he began fiddling with Sister's room door, I helped him to open it, and shut him in. He subsequently caused havoc there, before being straight-jacketed away to a mental hospital.

Night duty on Harley (emergency gynae) where the workload was all or nothing. In a 'nothing' stretch, marking a chalk cross on every creaking bit of the wooden floor; witnessing a delightful young company director eerily sleep-walking; assisting a spirited young German girl to look like a dolly bird, personalising her pre-op preparation.

Doing the 'eye drop' round with Sister Radcliffe and not being allowed to look at the 'blue boards' which showed the patient's prescription at the end of the bed. Instead of the usual double-checking procedure, she was expecting me (a student nurse) to do it all from memory. I thought she was helping me to unscrew a bottle, when she stiffened and looked daggers at me. It was her way of preventing me administering the wrong drops – and definitely not helping me!

Also on the Radcliffe Ward in the modern 'new block', I remember making pancakes on night duty using ingredients obtained from other 'new block' wards via the dumb waiter (normally used for transporting small items of equipment etc.) and distributing them the same way. Surprisingly we were never caught! When I left the ward Sister Radcliffe gave me a little tray. She called it a 'peace offering'. Have I still got it? I doubt it.

Night duty, men's medical, where a semi comatose Mr T received nightly visits from his lady friend. A small lady even in high heels, with long black wavy hair and heavily made up, she would announce her presence through the curtained double doors with a whispered, "Don't jump", and depart some time later after leaving traces of lipstick on Mr T's face, whilst screened by her long hair.

Maybury Mansions and the panic to be sufficiently uniformed before the coach left in the mornings. The nightly coffee socials where the slightest sound of jollifications would cause the warden to come scurrying up to appeal for quiet in no uncertain terms!

Anne Runciman

My interview day had started so happily as my father, who was a vet in Cambridge, had made it a very special day for me in that he had taken the day off to escort me.

The Deputy Matron conducted my interview but the first request was for me to move the chair to a skylight window to open it. I wondered why I had been asked to do this – was it to check whether I took off my shoes first or had my tights got holes in them? I never did discover.

Then I was transferred to the medical room where I was asked to take off all my clothes. I was only just eighteen and very shy and was told to turn around 360 degrees. I can honestly say that it was the most mortifying experience of my life, as I was not at all used it being naked in front of strangers. I left the room in a flummox and found that I had left my handbag behind, so I had to go back and collect it, which was the 'icing on the cake' in my distress. I thought then that it would have been much better for me to have applied to St Thomas' Hospital, as for that interview you only needed to write an essay.

To top it all I was soon ushered into a small room to do an intelligence test. This was because, due to illness, I had not got enough grades in my two A-levels. I'd never done an intelligence test before in my life, and I was terrified that I would not make that grade. I did pass it. After I staggered out of this experience, my father took me to the famous fish restaurant Sheekey's in nearby Fleet Street, but sadly I was too shaken to enjoy it.

I loved nursing and received a lovely compliment from one of the patients on my first ward, Dalziel. I had returned promptly at 1pm from days off when I walked in and one of the men shouted down the ward, "Thank goodness you're back Nurse Runciman, now we'll get a decent cup of tea!" All I could feel was a sense of terror that Sister had heard this comment and thought that I had been putting an extra teabag in the pot (I still remember that it was eight teabags in the big pot). Another time I felt terror was when my fellow student nurse Jackie McDevitt

Outside Piggott's Manor Back L–R: Alice Colby, Sarah Johnson, Jan Bramley, Lynn Grainger and Anne Runciman. Front L–R: Irene Collings and Elaine Fullard.

Matron's Ball John Cooke and Anne Runciman pictured at one of the Balls. They married in 1968.

thought that she had got a wasp in her bra. I set about helping Jackie to strip off her clothes in the sluice and was so frightened that Sister would come in to find me in the act and with Jackie half undressed...

Other memories are how grateful I am that someone had thought to enliven the long bleak underground corridor from the main Bart's building to the new QE II block on the other side of Little Britain Street. All along this corridor were hung paintings by the Great Masters. I vowed to learn one painting per night as I passed on my way to night duty on the Neurology Ward. Since then I have had no difficulty in answering the art questions on *University Challenge*.

As my fellow Bart's friends know, I normally wouldn't 'say boo to a goose' but there were two occasions where my brave self showed. The first one was when a friend who had gone to University to read chemistry at Westfield College invited me to a debate 'University Fits You For Life'. The audience, who were the same age as me, all seemed so complacent, arrogant and self-satisfied that I rose up and said, "You are not learning about life. I have been nursing both a tramp and a Lord of the Realm today and think that equips me much better for life on the same intellectual level as you", and sat down with a bump!

Another time I spoke out was when, as a staff nurse, I was making a bed with Sister Mary (who I adored) and said something (I can't remember what) that I strongly disagreed with and said so, whereupon Sister Mary let out a long, "Ooooooooooh – still waters do run deep."

There were so many treats, though, outside hospital life. The London theatre staff used to hand in spare tickets to the Nurses' Home to be distributed free to us, so that at one point I had seen all the best plays that were on in London.

I married John Cooke (a doctor) in 1968 and had already had my first child by the time we were awarded our belts at Prizegiving. My mother came to hold the baby while we had our photographs taken.

In conclusion, the best thing for me from our time at Bart's are the friendships that we formed through joys and hardships that we experienced, so that fifty-five years on we can just pick up where we were since our shared background goes so deep.

Liz Senter

As a child, apart from being a fireman, my only ambition was to be a nurse. This was hardly surprising as my father was a doctor, my mother an ex-Bart's nurse and my grandmother had been a nurse. I only applied to Bart's and I wonder what I would have done if I had not been accepted? In fact, a contemporary at school with a similar pedigree was turned down.

My friendships began even before starting my training – I met Sarah at interview and Elaine whilst apple picking to fill in time before PTS.

Liz Senter.

Our bond developed and we formed a merry camaraderie. One morning, we dressed up the skeleton used for teaching (whose name nobody can remember) in a nurse's uniform and sat him or her in the front row of the class, ready for Miss Nicholls' lesson. At first she didn't notice it as it had got a hat well pushed down on its skull. We were all 'in stitches' and I don't recall the final outcome.

Piggott's Manor was a time of fun and on occasion I found myself in trouble. We socialized with the 'boys' at the nearby Elstree flying school, visiting the local pub with them. Imagine our delight/horror when, sometime after 'lights out', there was the sound of guitar and song coming from an open topped sports car driving around under our windows! I was one of those summoned to answer for my actions the following morning and clearly remember being asked, "What would your parents think of you in a public house?" I felt that I could not say that they would be delighted!

My ambition to be a fireman stood me in good stead when the local fire officer came to lecture us and I was reprimanded by him for fooling around. I felt duly ashamed and when he wanted a volunteer to abseil out of a window felt duty bound to offer my services!

I started on Mary, the first ward that my mother proudly told me that she had started on. I found the whole experience very challenging at first. I lacked confidence and I was very diffident and fearful of doing things wrong. This made it difficult to use my own initiative. Life after Mary became even worse when I went to Bowlby. Sister Bowlby had something of a reputation! I remember, what seemed like many night hours, cleaning and polishing bedpans in the sluice. However, the steely Senter spirit prevailed and I survived the first six months!

Bart's provided us with an extraordinary mix of experiences. We nursed the 'semi permanent residents of the Embankment' alongside the aristocracy. I nursed George Sassoon and now find myself living in the Somerset village where his father is buried. I first encountered drug abuse, whilst assisting a young man to inject himself with heroin – on the ward where the 'grey lady' walked!

Christmas was fun. I remember, as staff nurse on Harmsworth, making large cardboard cutout snowmen to put up around the ward. There was something of a competitive spirit which prevailed and we really did think that our decorations that year were the best!

Night duty on Pitcairn was one of the most cheerful times of my life! I worked with a wonderfully funny third year and we spent most of the eleven hours together laughing. I so well remember watching the mice come out to play on the polished wooden floorboards. They, of course, were given names like 'anonymouse', 'magnanimouse', 'minimouse' and so on! And then, as we went through the tunnel to break in the dining room, we would count the cockroaches. The joy of life before health and safety...

I learned the joy of travel and not a year went by without at least two trips abroad. It was a good way to team up with a different group of friends depending upon who was free to go. We had some very enterprising holidays and our photo albums are full of the reminders. Despite small pay packets we seemed to have funds for the things that mattered.

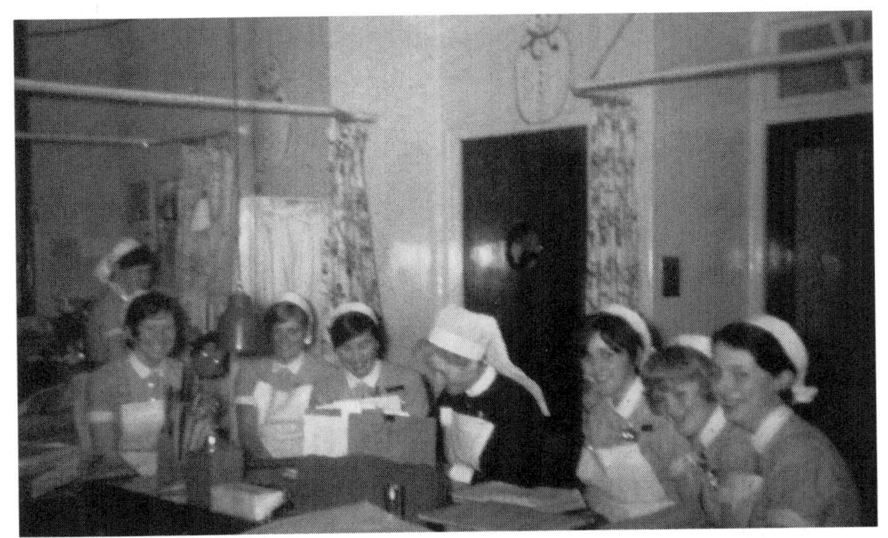

Christmas on Harmsworth Ward
Top: Staff gathered around the Christmas tree.
Bottom: Sister Hall, better known as 'Fairy', flanked by young nurses.
Note the cardboard snowmen made by Staff Nurse, Liz Senter.

This has been an illuminating experience for me. Having worked in different types of nursing both here and abroad I had spent the last seventeen years working as a hospice nurse within the NHS. I felt that bedside nursing was the thing that I cherished most and my skills lay in communicating with people. By the time I left on retirement I had reached the point of wondering why I had ever become a nurse. Now I remember!

Ruth Shrubbs

A contribution by her husband, Peter Fulford

As many of you know, Ruth's Alzheimers is now at an advanced stage and she has been in a specialist care home since November 2017. Elaine suggested that perhaps I might contribute a few lines on her behalf.

Alongside her family (three children, seven grandchildren), music and singing, nursing was always a fundamental interest.

I met Ruth in 1967 when she was in Gloucester House, next door to Bart's. Later, she moved to Maybury Mansions in Marylebone. I remember well collecting her from there in my battered and reliably unreliable Austin Healey. We often went in the evening to the nearby Bistro in Crawford Street.

Ruth regularly attended the two Bart's churches – St Bartholomew-the-Great and St Bartholomew-the-Less. Singing was a particular joy and wherever we lived she always joined the local church choir and/or choral society.

Singing was a particular joy of Ruth's
L-R: Ruth Shrubbs, Anne Behn (a friend of Elaine's from Germany), Elaine Fullard.

Sunbathing Ruth Shrubbs and Alice Colby on the balcony of Queen Mary's Nurses' Home.

We married in September 1968 and the powers that be thoughtfully put her on night duty for the preceding six months to get it out of the way!

Going back to the beginning of her nursing career, before I knew her, Ruth spent her first few months at Piggott's Manor in Letchmore Heath, near Radlett. She liked to recount her memory of walking into Radlett for shops or the train and passing a small cluster of 1930s red brick houses and thinking to herself, one of those would be a nice place to live. Actually, one of those was my childhood family home and some twenty years later we bought that house and brought up our family there!

Needless to say, Ruth loved her happy times at Bart's with all of you and would have been looking forward to joining you in February.

Anne Spooner

I remember...

- Being interviewed by Miss Stonehouse, Deputy Matron. Meeting Rosemary, Sandy and Shelagh for the first time at Aldenham Cottage.
- Taking forty-five minutes to put my uniform on for the first time. All my hats were subsequently made by Shelagh.
- Eating doughnuts at Piggott's Manor whilst listening to Peter, Paul and Mary and the Dave Clark Five.
- Being inspected before going to Bart's for the first time – half hair showing, hem length eighteen inches from the floor and very short fingernails.
- Going to Covent Garden at 6am to buy flowers for View Day.
- Cleaning – lockers, bed wheels, the sluice and bedpans.
- Always addressing patients, medical staff and nursing colleagues by their surnames.
- Being reprimanded for making too much noise with teaspoons whilst serving coffee during Sir Ronald Bodley Scott's ward round.
- Sister Stanmore refusing to have Antony Armstrong-Jones as a patient on her ward as his presence would disturb the other patients.
- Nursing James Paterson Ross on Percival Pott Ward. His father had operated on my father in 1947 when he'd developed tracheal stenosis following extensive radiotherapy treatment at Guy's hospital during the 1930s.
- Ward Sisters who, during the year, kept a record in the ward diary of elderly patients who lived alone locally and were re-admitted on Christmas Eve to spend Christmas with company rather than being alone.

- Singing carols at Christmas in the wards with cloaks turned around to show the red lining.
- Carrying my possessions in a wicker basket.
- Going on holiday to Yugoslavia with Liz, Di, Chris and Katie. A night flight followed by a day by the pool. Di fell asleep in the sun and was quite badly burnt.
- Wondering how we ever slept in the flat in Smithfield as the market worked throughout the night and it was so noisy.
- Wearing a fifth year hat for a short time before leaving Bart's to do my Part I Midwifery training.
- Four years of good nursing practice – lots of laughter, sadness at the loss of patients, and above all friendships which continue.

Patients I recall

- The lady from Jersey who had had a Wertheim's hysterectomy and had no appetite post-operatively.
- Mr Howkins prescribed Champagne tds (three times a day).
- Jonathan, an eighteen-month-old, whose pram had slipped from the platform at a tube station. He spent months on Kenton with a foot injury.
- The elderly lady with inoperable breast cancer. Hilary McCruddon, the Staff Nurse, taught me how to do her daily dressings.

Ann Stringfellow

I went for my interview on 15th October 1964. It was Election Day but I don't have any recollection of knowing that at the time. I think the fear of the interview took all my thoughts. Maggie Powell and Anne Runciman were there as well. I remember my mother chatting to Mrs Powell but I don't remember much about the day apart from us all being asked to open a window. I never worked out why that was.

I had the choice of Tommy's, Westminster or Bart's and I chose well, I think. Partly, my decision was based on the history of Bart's and I felt that I would be at home coming from Oxford. The more important reason at the time was frivolous – I would be near my boyfriend who lived in Edgware if I went to PTS in Letchmore Heath.

February 8th came and I really wanted to arrive by train but my parents insisted that they deliver me in the car. I thought everybody else would have made their friends on the train. It was such excitement to arrive and find my room, sharing with Liz Goodchild who I thought was so sensible and kind.

I think we all remember having our uniforms fitted and adjusted, and the cap going on for the first time. Do you remember Mary Tuckwell drowning under her cap? I had an argument with one of our sister tutors about the length of the hem. They measured eighteen inches from the ground, which for Mary meant on her knee or near, whereas my hem was practically down to the floor, or so it felt.

I had always wanted to go to boarding school so PTS was a dream come true. I was very happy to stay at the weekends and found it strange that most people seemed to want to go home.

My first ward was Colston and Elaine Fullard was my companion there. It was a very happy place and Sister was really kind. I heard horror stories of other sisters and dreaded moving but Sister Waring was again a caring and jolly leader.

I know now that I was very silly in not making enough effort to learn more about London, visit the museums, or go to the theatre or concerts. My life revolved round the hospital and social life. This seemed to consist of meetings for coffee after our shifts, or shopping trips to Oxford Street, or the latest party which all blur into one from this distance in time.

I remember Sister Pitcairn being incensed when she heard a patient use my first name, scolding me enough to cry, and her sending me to get the tea as a punishment. It was no punishment because her teas consisted of sandwiches and little fancy cakes. We all sneaked the odd crust. I never found out how the patient knew my name as no one called me anything but Stringy.

Do you remember the old lift in the Gynae block? It was run by steam I believe.

We used to follow the health of patients who had been there a long time, and we would ask after them when we had moved on from the ward. Mr Hamlet was one such who lived on W. G. Grace. He was beautifully looked after and we all hoped he would regain consciousness but he never did.

My nursing career fell into two parts. Before children, I specialised in theatre work, and when I returned to nursing after fourteen years, I was lucky to find a research nurse post in Gastroenterology. From that I grasped an opportunity to develop my role into a Hepatology Specialist Nurse.

There are so many memories but the best gift of all from Bart's was to have made so many lifetime friends. We are so lucky. Nurses today do not have anything like the good times that we had. I can hear my late mother speaking because she said exactly the same of her generation.

Cecilia Thoday

I remember going to Letchmore Heath to Piggott's Manor on the appointed day with my father and, for some reason, my then boy-friend Robin. It was like going to a convent or the like, as if I was never going to see my family or Robin again. Of course we were able to go home not long after we started. I remember Libby Thomas came to stay with me for a weekend as she lived so far away in Wales.

We learned how to do proper bandaging of limbs and stomach binders etc. There was a huge life sized doll, one of the training dummies, called Angelina Bartholomew, who we made comfortable and treated like a real person. We soon progressed to visits to the hospital for ward experience. My first ward was to be Lucas which was the children's ward. Sister Lucas had a reputation of being very strict but I always found her to be very fair. I remember a baby on the ward with a diagnosis of 'Battered Baby syndrome'. I asked what that meant and was shocked to be told the baby had actually been battered. I simply did not understand that some people would hurt their babies.

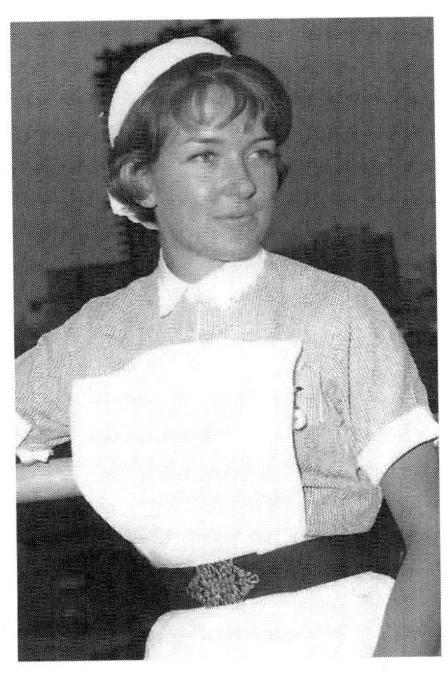

Cecilia Thoday Pictured in 1968.

I moved on from Lucas to Luke Ward which dealt with blood disorders and where the patients were sometimes very ill. I did well on Luke Ward as bedside nursing was my forte. Old Sister Luke was an absolute angel; she was serene and gentle. I remember being very happy there. Then came the time for changing wards – where would I go for my last ward as a junior probationer? Yes you guessed it, my next ward was Bowlby a male surgical ward. Sister Bowlby had a fearsome reputation and she did shout at me several times. The incident I remember most and still is in my mind is the butter under the grill. The juniors had to do the bread and butter mid afternoon for tea. If the butter had been in the fridge and therefore needed softening we would put the grill on for a few minutes to just warm it up. I, of course, forgot the grill was on and the butter was now melted all over the floor and no longer any use for the bread. I can still hear her shouting, "Thoday". She did not need to say anything else I was a gibbering wreck. Still, I survived Sister Bowlby and the rest of my training.

About to be married Cecilia Thoday on her Wedding Day in 1969, at Gloucester House.

Of course for me the worst thing I remember from Bart's was my mother being taken ill and we were referred to Professor Howkins who was a professor of Gynae medicine. My father and I went to the clinic where my mother was examined by Professor Howkins. I remember him coming out of the examination room and coming to me rather than my father and he just shook his head in sadness knowing it would be almost impossible to save her life. Professor Howkins did all he could to try and save my mother. She underwent surgery and radiotherapy and was in Pitcairn Ward for three months. My mother lived for another year and then became very unwell again and returned to Pitcairn Ward where she died on 15th March 1968, just a few days after we qualified as State Registered Nurses.

My best memory of Bart's was being married at St Bartholomew-the-Great church eighteen months after my mother had died.

Cecilia Thoday and Chris Hale's wedding in St Bartholomew-the-Great, London's oldest parish church The church has appeared in a number of award-winning films and was the location for the 'fourth wedding' in *Four Weddings and a Funeral*.

A few extra memories from Bart's days

Do you remember all the initial language that we learned like:

TTAs – Drugs to take home.
DDAs – Drugs under the dangerous drugs act.
WOPs, MOPs, SOPs for Women's outpatients, Medical outpatients, Surgical outpatients, etc.
BID – Brought in dead.
RTA – Road traffic accident.
DNR – Do not resuscitate.
STC – Special treatment centre.

The STC would now be called the sexually transmitted disease clinic I expect. I worked there after my mother died. I think they tried to put me where I would not meet patients that were dying from cancer, in order not to distress me. Sister Sinclair was fanatical about cleanliness. She said, "Make this place and all the instruments spotless so that you would not mind them being used on you". I remember patients were called by a number and not a name. And I found it strange that men had picked up syphilis from other men. How naive I was in those days.

I remember the ward basket which was used to do the rounds in the morning. Collecting the post. Delivering prescriptions and collecting them. What a nice job that was when it was quiet, to escape into the square and do the rounds.

Anne Thomas

I had wanted to be a nurse ever since I was five when a neighbour I admired told me she was going to be a nurse. Having been frustrated by a back injury caused by playing hockey at school which made me choose to go to a teacher training college rather than apply to a hospital, I found myself at twenty not wanting to be a primary school teacher at all, thereby making me the eldest in our February 1965 Set.

I applied to Bart's and to Leeds Infirmary, not feeling that Bart's would ever take *me*. I'd already had my interview at Leeds (where I had been welcomed by a friendly Home Sister wearing a Bart's badge who, I later learned, was Pat Churchman's mother!) and been accepted, so didn't feel too nervous for my interview at Bart's.

I'd gone up to London on the train from Hitchin and had walked from the St Paul's tube station looking for the entrance to the hospital. I was rather shocked to see so many doctors walking around with their bloody aprons on out in the street near the main entrance, as I thought it wasn't very hygienic. It was only much later that I discovered there was a very famous meat market called Smithfield just opposite. (Of course nowadays we would have looked up the area on the internet!). I found my way to the Nurses' Home, I must have arrived early, and then the wait started, sitting with a few others in a little room. This was where I met Sandra Whitehouse for the first time and we must have had quite a long time to talk to each other as when we ended up starting on the same day and being in the same Set, I felt as though I knew her well. I quite enjoyed the interview, I don't remember the medical at all (perhaps too traumatized by being asked to stand naked) and I do remember doing the 'tests' which was when I was sure I'd fail.

When I was accepted I was elated and said how sorry I was to Leeds and then looked for something to do until we started. I'd already passed the eighteen years and six months maturity mark. Now I was nervous. Going off with my suitcase again on the train (I can't think why my father didn't take me as we lived fairly near; maybe I didn't want him too, I can't

Fully Qualified L–R: Lynn Grainger, Anne Thomas, Alice Colby, Liz Senter and Sarah Johnson. Note the Bart's badges.

remember). I do remember being in the same carriage as another young lady who was with her mother and whom I felt was also going to same place. As I slowly followed them (they didn't seem to be in a hurry), we were indeed going to the same place and it was of course Stephanie Norbury and her mother.

When we arrived I was rather upset at having the privilege of having a room on my own as everyone else had someone to talk over the events of the day, except perhaps Irene and some other mature student nurses! Despite my experience of living in hall at college, away from home, Piggott's Manor was rather daunting and not at all like the real world to me. I couldn't really follow that playing with mannequins and injecting into oranges was preparing me to care for patients, but the bed making, yes. What was happening was that we were being *trained*; knocked into shape, helped to understand that discipline was going to be obeying the Ward Sister...

Once I got to the hospital I enjoyed it all: the sore feet, the aching legs, the fear that I thought I could let somebody die if I forgot to do something, the fear of being found chatting in the sluice... I enjoyed being with the patients, my friends, the team on the wards, making a tidy bed quickly and efficiently, the long talks in our bedrooms with the mugs of cocoa or instant coffee, the choir, the swimming pool, the free theatre tickets, taking the patients out into the square in their beds, the kettles boiling all night for cups of tea (in France, they still don't believe that people asked for tea to help them go back to sleep!).

My first ward was Radcliffe where our first responsibility was to measure 'the fluids' in and out. I was of course nervous giving my first injection for a patient after the oranges, but at least the person couldn't see my worried face. Much later my first job in France was at a specialist ophthalmology clinic in Nantes – by this time I was putting drops in eyes and much more besides. The way we were coached through procedures and gradually taking more and more responsibility helped me gain confidence although night duty could be quite nerve-racking! Those eight nights on with four nights off for three consecutive months were so exhausting. I found it hard to stay awake at night and difficult to sleep during the day. A nightmare indeed!

I think the turning point in my training came in my second year on Annie Zunz with Miss Bartlett as Sister. It was here that I was confronted with a sudden death as I helped a lady onto a commode. The way Miss Bartlett talked me through the shock explaining that a huge pulmonary embolus wasn't my fault put me on the right path to finding my way to working in palliative care for twenty years until I retired.

Miss Joan Loveridge Matron and Superintendent of Nursing. Pictured on View Day by Anne Thomas' father.

Libby Thomas

At my interview Miss Loveridge asked me to close the window, which I duly did with a bang, must have been an adrenaline rush! I wonder if anybody else was asked?

One of the male board members asked me what sports I'd played at school, and when I mentioned cricket, he said, "Oh they really are out of the caves in Wales then", which probably contributed to my response of, "Second cave on the left after Bristol", when asked by the same gentleman where I lived! Miss Loveridge was quietly amused and nodded her head intimating that I would do. She did apologise privately to me for his comment, and we always had a mutual respect for each other from that day.

This was really tested,however, when I was caught coming back late one night without a late pass. When the night porter at the gate asked my name for his book I said, 'Lily White', inspired by the boxes of said unmentionables stacked awaiting delivery to stores! Next morning I was called to Matron's office, I'd been spotted by Night Sister crossing the square and she had checked the porter's book! Oh dear, I was mortified! Miss Loveridge was furious at first but struggled not to laugh when I explained why I'd chosen Lily White! She then told me that I could not have a late pass for a month and if I was deceitful again she would inform my mother. I never let either of them down again!

I. Ranger, Esq., M.S., F.R.C.S.
G. S. Thompson, Esq., M.D., M.A., M.R.C.P.

Miss B. Champney, S.R.N., R.N.T.
Miss E. Raybould, S.R.N., R.N.T.

FINAL STATE EXAMINATION FOR THE GENERAL PART OF THE REGISTER.

1962 EXPERIMENTAL SYLLABUS

Monday, 29th January, 1968.

MORNING.

ALL ASPECTS OF NURSING CARE AND TREATMENT OF PATIENTS
(included in the Syllabus of Training)

Time allowed 3 hours.

IMPORTANT. *Read the questions carefully, and answer only what is asked in the sections as indicated, as no credit will be given for irrelevant matter. The percentages shown on the right of this paper denote the proportion of weighting allocated to each section of the question.*

NOTE. Candidates MUST attempt FIVE questions and not more than five.

1. (*a*) Describe the clinical features of heart failure. 30%
   (*b*) What are the causes of heart failure? 20%
   (*c*) Describe the nursing care and treatment of a patient with heart failure. 50%
2. What are the dangers and side effects of the following drugs:—
   (*a*) Aspirin;
   (*b*) Barbiturates;
   (*c*) Oral contraceptives;
   (*d*) Morphine;
   (*e*) Chloramphenicol;
   (*f*) Cortico steroids?

   Equal % for each part
3. A middle-aged man has been admitted to hospital for investigation of severe headache.
   (*a*) List the possible causes. 20%
   (*b*) What investigations may be undertaken and how may the nurse help with these? 40%
   (*c*) What would you do to help this man when his headache is severe? 40%
4. (*a*) Describe the physiology of micturition. 30%
   (*b*) Give an account of the disorders of micturition which may be encountered in a male. 40%
   (*c*) Describe the nursing care of a patient with an indwelling urethral catheter. 30%
5. A middle-aged woman is admitted to hospital with anaemia, haemoglobin 50% (7.4 G/100 mls).
   (*a*) What is haemoglobin? Describe its function. 10%
   (*b*) What observations would you make of this patient on admission? 30%
   (*c*) What investigations may be ordered? 20%
   (*d*) Give an account of the causes of anaemia in a middle-aged woman. 40%
6. What are the responsibilities of the staff nurse in charge of a ward with regard to:—
   (*a*) the admission of a very ill patient; 40%
   (*b*) this patient's personal property; 30%
   (*c*) this patient's relatives? 30%

Examination paper Our final State Registered Nurse examination paper, January 1968.

Mary Tuckwell

I remember nothing of my interview except the medical, with the doctor telling me I was the smallest five foot and half an inch he had ever met. I had only applied to Bart's (out of ignorance) and was very afraid they wouldn't have me if I told them I was only five foot. I was also slightly appalled when a friend of my mother's said it was Tommy's for ladies, Guy's for wives and Bart's for tarts!

PTS was just like the school I had just left but with more freedom, so I was very happy, I think. I am sure it was the closeness of us all by the time we left PTS that made the rest so good for me and the fact that I feel I know every one of us is a friend not just a classmate.

Bart's, itself, was much more scary but Sister Pitcairn was such an eccentric that I was fascinated by her and remember my first ward probably better than any other. She was so determined to avoid saying goodbye to the rather posher women patients that she frequently left the ward by the fire escape. I loved that she thought it important to have nice china at tea time for women who might be feeling they had lost their femininity. I was also very annoyed that she thought I was too young to listen to John Howkins' ward round in case he told rude jokes.

I think I loved all wards until I got to Bowlby just after qualifying. "I had heard you were small but this is ridiculous. We have two 'belts', go and clean the windowsills, the maid is ill." It wasn't a promising start. I was terrified of her, useless at authority and had a miserable three months (including nearly killing someone with *Senokot*) before going back to theatres – which I loved!

My main regret is that I made so little use of London and anything outside Bart's while I was there.

Prizegiving in the Great Hall, 1969
Back L–R: Anne Spooner, Liz Woodger, Wendy Williams, Liz Senter, Sarah Johnson, Ruth Shrubbs, Lynn Grainger, Irene Collings, Mary-Anne de Vere, Alice Colby, Heather White.

Middle L–R: Anne Berry, Jean Gaunt, Chris Bailey, Dorothy Clarkson, Jackie McDevitt, Cecilia Thoday, Josephine, Chris Cook, Elaine Fullard, Jan Bramley.

Front L–R: Adrea Ripley, Katie Lees, Gill Hayward, Anne Runciman, Sue Shouler, Rosemary Chaplin.

Heather White

I have no recollection of being stripped naked for my medical, unlike Anne Runciman, but I do remember a rather dishy blond Registrar who did the medical. I had decided not to apply to St Thomas' because they wanted an essay – not appreciated when you're still at school. Following the interview I seem to remember that we were measured for our uniform; a skirt that swept the floor; big black shoes etc. My parents still remember taking me to PTS; the door was opened, I was told to come in and the door was promptly slammed in their faces.

I remember PTS as being a happy time with memories of *Little Boxes* by Nina and Frederick and *Take Five* by Dave Brubeck. We had cookery classes and I remember producing a perfectly shaped poached egg on toast which I had to take on a tray for the senior sister tutor to admire! Bandaging in the billiard room. Almost fainting when we watched the films of mine rescues. The rest is a blank.

Heather White Pictured by the lifts in Charterhouse Nurses' Home.

I remember that we had to have late passes if we wanted to stay out after 10pm and trying to find a phone box to say that I was going to be late having watched a film that went on longer than expected.

During my first year, on the day I started on one of the children's wards, I arrived to find a child screaming in his cot. On bending over to comfort him I lost my cap just as Sister walked in. She was furious because I hadn't got my cap on but unconcerned about the screaming child. I don't know if anyone else remembers pushing cockroaches out of the sluice room with mops every time it rained.

My second year started on James Gibb where I met my husband-to-be while he was having his knee sorted by Jackson-Burrows. Most of the time I was on night duty and the fit young men played havoc most nights. One morning I side-stepped a glass of water being thrown at me in retaliation for pouring water over a very healthy patient, only to have it land on the night report book on Sister's desk. I survived.

Whilst doing my practical for the SRN I was asked to put a patient in a suitable position for a certain (can't remember what) procedure. Having arranged the patient as per Winifred Hector's book the examiner said, "How ridiculous!"

When I took my Bart's oral exam I remember a long conversation about Trench Foot. I can't say I've seen much of this since – most useful.

The following are just a few things of which I have fond memories

- The lift in the George V block.
- The flower shop.
- View Days – all those flowers.
- Walking to work from Charterhouse Square through the meat market – always feeling safe.
- Free tickets to the theatres.
- The Balls at College Hall.
- Glandular Fever and being in sickrooms.
- Sitting around the Fountain.

One will always remember certain patients for differing reasons. The man from the Royal Household with his royal purple towels with gold insignia or the down-and-out with jumping fleas.

When I was a Pink on the Metabolic Unit a whole new world opened up on the top floor, where Clinical Pharmacology had row upon row of floppy eared bunny rabbits and willing students as guinea pigs as well as the professors themselves.

Sandra Whitehouse

The first day at PTS (Piggott's Manor) I stood quaking on the mat and was very relieved when Katie Lees turned up to share my fate. We were soon into the humiliating business of trying on our new uniform. The sister tutor was determined that my dress and apron should be flapping frumpily round my calves and that my hat tails should be drooping round the nape of the neck and fixed firmly low down on my brow. Katie, being small and neat, seemed to be getting a better deal. Below the knee was approved for her. Later, on the wards, I discovered that uniform was a very distinguishing factor and that we probationers could be spotted a mile off by the way we wore ours. We soon learned and Steph Norbury was at the forefront, trend setting with shorter hem lengths (shrunk at the laundry) and tiny neat caps set on the back of the head. Her tiny waist was legendary!

PTS was a great time for Set bonding. I think we knew then that laughter and sticking together would be a great defence. I never see Tom Jones without remembering us all in the big sitting room watching *Top of the Pops*. He had just finished *Delilah*, resplendent in his open white shirt, revealing his black hairy chest, when Di sighed, "Ooh hasn't he got a lovely body!"

First ward first day! I was sent off to light the oven, a gas monster. I wasn't at all familiar with ovens at the time and certainly not gas ones. The contemptuous ward maid showed me the pilot light lurking in the deep recesses and I turned it on and went in search of the matches. There was a loud explosive bang, I fell back on my heels and most of the plates fell to the floor, bringing Sister, who was in the middle of the report, into the kitchen. She sent me off to enquire how many minutes all thirty-two patients wanted their eggs. I soon learned to write it all down and boil them all for four minutes. No one complained!

I once nursed Miss Hector, the principal sister tutor; that was a case for shaky hands and first ward nerves all over again. But as a patient the only complaint she made to me was that I must remember to stand her toast upright before I butter it. I do it every day because just like all those detailed procedures it's the best way!

I was lucky to have Lynn Grainger to share first ward terrors with. We were always keen to perform any new procedure which could then be crossed off in those practical procedure books. You name it, we were up for it: tubes and drains from all orifices; gory dressings; removal of stitches. Who was it who volunteered to have a Riles tube passed on them? Brave girl.

On one occasion I had removal of stitches from scrotum on my tasks for the day. I was naturally nervous. We, as a group of eighteen-year-old girls, many of us from single-sex boarding schools, had little knowledge of the male body and how it worked. I appeared in the sluice doorway red and flustered and said to Lynn, "He's got one of those things." She said, "What things?" Sister appeared in the doorway and, overhearing, seized a bottle of ether and marched down the ward. She soon came swishing triumphant from behind the curtain having doused the offending member. I, as the unfortunate student, then had to proceed. The young man was very apologetic.

Sister Fleet Street ran a tight ship. Our hands were split and raw from carbolising the beds and sterilising the bottles. One morning I came on duty with a bit of a headache and the previous night's eye make up still in evidence. During report I could see she had spotted me, so I kept looking up so that she wouldn't see the eye shadow. I was sent off to wash my face. During the same week a houseman was told to get a hair cut before setting foot on her ward again. Everyone had to polish their shoes daily.

Lynn and I had our hour of glory when we were left on the ward by ourselves and dealt with a pulmonary embolism – mainly by getting Sister at once.

Night duty had some moments. Beth and I were on Neurosurgery. No one ever seemed to get better. It was really hard and sometimes we were reduced to hysteria by those nutty nights. There were a lot of patients with bedsides and one in particular with a nifty habit of grabbing you by the apron and, with amazing strength, almost dragging you into bed with him. We saved each other when possible. We also used to run down the ward to catch the bottles before they hit the deck.

It was freezing in the recovery room and no cardigans allowed even when icing the sheets.

When I was on Surgery Ward one of our Set was wheeled in on a trolley on a quiet night feigning advanced labour. I felt totally panicked.

Wedding Day
Nurses lined the Square when Sandra Whitehouse married Tim Stephenson. She was the first of the Set to marry, in October 1967.

I also recall that I once threw out a soiled pair of trousers because I just couldn't face them and had to own up in the morning when the patient was sober.

Looking back at my time at Barts it certainly represents some of the most significant years of my life. We were very young to bear a lot of responsibility (I am thinking particularly of being in charge at night on a coronary care at the beginning of my second year) whilst at the same time being treated like children concerning nurses home regulations.

I think youth was on our side in terms of sheer stamina as nursing then was very physical and split shifts made for very long days. Youth made us both vulnerable and resilient to the new experiences of death and suffering. Vulnerable in that it was so new and, resilient in that it seemed then so far removed (for most of us) from our own experience and from anything we could imagine would happen to us.

What now remains after all this time is the ability always to find humour a great relief, even amongst sadness. Also the ability to prioritise and work quickly when there are a lot of practical tasks to be done. No task is too menial as I started off cleaning the lavatories at Piggott's Manor.

But first and foremost the patients will never be forgotten, either for their courage or their humour or their acceptance. We had a wide catchment area at Barts. I nursed a Reverend Mother who called her imaginary nuns for compline each evening; an ex-governor of Australia who demanded port after dinner; and, the actress who played Maria's mother from *The Sound of Music*, who showered us with theatre tickets.

I am compelled to carry with me always Mr Butler who suffered, what was then particularly horrible treatment for tongue cancer so cheerfully, a young woman with extreme exfoliative dermatitis because of an antibiotic allergy, whom I barrier nursed on a mattress on the floor, where she sadly died surrounded by photos of her children and, a bedridden old man who had wasted away to six stone, whom we cradled in our arms whilst turning.

Finally, Christmas at Bart's. A few nurses with scores to settle captured a young houseman, held him aloft and dumped him in the fountain. He went off waving and bowing. On nights, on Christmas Eve, we felt the need to celebrate, whilst quiet, and invited our compatriots from the opposite ward for a night cap. Brandy from the medicine cupboard in medicine glasses – you can't beat it! On hearing Night Sister coming unexpectedly back down the corridor we opened the drawer and carefully placed all four glasses on top of a chart, then closed it. She hovered around, opened the drawer for the chart and took the glasses out, placing them carefully on the desk. When she was finished she replaced each one slowly, being sure not to spill them. Having closed the drawer she wished us a happy Christmas and made off again down the corridor.

Highlight of the Year – Matron's Ball

Liz Woodger and Chris Cooke with partners.

GH

THE ROYAL
HOSPITAL OF ST. BARTHOLOMEW

Nurses' Dance

Menu

La Crème Portugaise

Le Suprême de Turbotin d'Antin

Le Carré d'Agneau Rôti Dubarry
Les Haricots Verts Fins
Les Pommes Dorées

La Poire de Comice Belle Hélène
Le Parfait Glacé Vanille

Le Café

Grosvenor House — 4th January, 1967

"Weeks before, medical students would be flaunting themselves for an invitation"

L-R: Alice Colby, Ruth Shrubbs, Sarah Johnson, Elaine Fullard and Liz Senter with partners.

L-R: Anne Berry, Jackie McDevitt and Liz Woodger with partners.

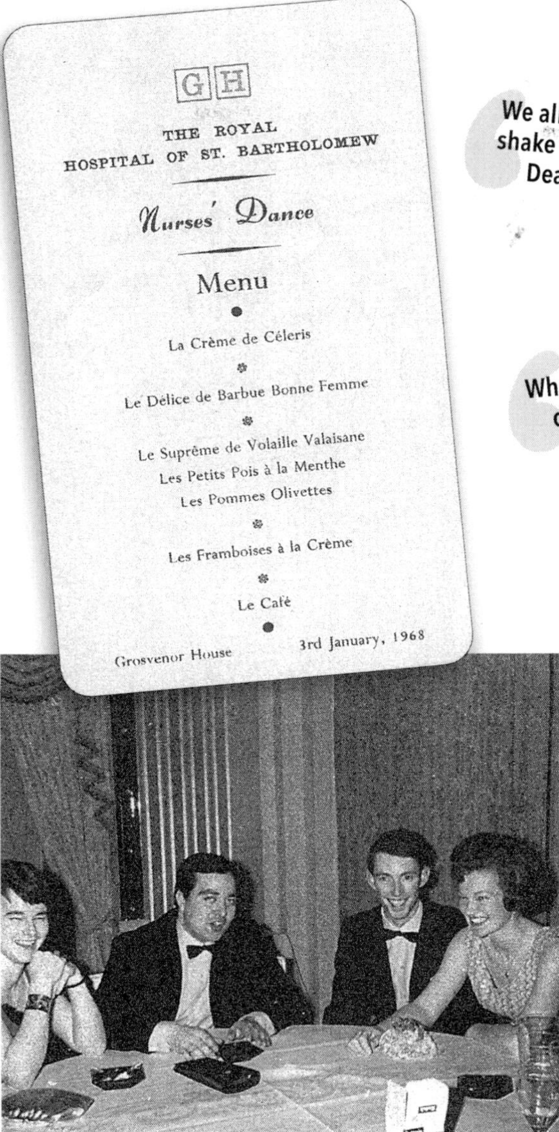
GH

THE ROYAL
HOSPITAL OF ST. BARTHOLOMEW

Nurses' Dance

Menu

La Crème de Céleris

Le Délice de Barbue Bonne Femme

Le Suprême de Volaille Valaisane
Les Petits Pois à la Menthe
Les Pommes Olivettes

Les Framboises à la Crème

Le Café

Grosvenor House 3rd January, 1968

“We all had to wear long gloves to shake hands with Matron and the Dean of the Medical School”

“What excitement – planning outfits for Matron's Ball”

Pat Churchman and Jan Bramley with partners.

L–R: Cecilia Thoday, Jackie McDevitt, Jean Gaunt, Anne Berry and Dorf Clarkson with partners.

L–R: Alice Colby, Ruth Shrubbs, Anne Thomas, Sarah Johnson and Liz Senter with partners. Peter Fulford (to the right of Ruth Shrubbs) became her husband and contributed a memoir on Ruth's behalf (see page 75).

Matron's Ball 1969 L–R: Ann Stringfellow, Gill Hayward (behind), Heather White, Maggie Powell and Mary Tuckwell with partners.

"People jumping into the fountain after a Ball"

The Treasurer and Governors
of
Saint Bartholomew's Hospital
request the pleasure of the company of

Miss Anne Thomas

on Wednesday, 15th January, 1969
at Grosvenor House, Park Lane

GREAT ROOM
ENTRANCE PARK LANE

R.S.V.P. Matron
St. Bartholomew's Hospital,
London, E.C.1

Dancing 9 p.m. - 1.30 a.m.

THIS CARD <u>MUST</u> BE PRESENTED AT THE DOOR